ILLUSTRATIONS BY STU GROSS

BIOGRAPHY AND SONG COMMENTARIES BY ROBERT SHELTON

The Josh White Song Book

MUSIC EDITED BY WALTER RAIM   *Quadrangle Books | Chicago*

Contents

BY ROBERT SHELTON

The Josh White Story

1 — The Fighter

I done had my fun, if I don't get well no more,
I done had my fun, if I don't get well no more,
My health is failing me
And I know I'm going down slow.
                                        "Going Down Slow" Blues

THE WIND off the lake had died down. For Chicago in January it was surprisingly mild. It was Friday evening and the office workers heading home to the Near North Side were grateful for the weather and for Friday evening. But some men's dusk is other men's dawn. The neon signs of Rush Street's cabarets blinked the arrival of another week-end.

At the corner of Rush and Walton, five musicians, a few technicians and a straggle of watchers assembled in Studio A of the Universal Recording Company. Studio men busied themselves shifting microphones on booms that resembled angular metal flamingos waiting to be fed. The musicians ambled to their places.

Near the center of the room, a lean and darkly handsome man watched the preparations quietly. Thirty-five years, he thought. Who stole my time? Would I do it the same way again or would I be smarter? Maybe it wasn't so bad. I had my fun. I did some good.

It had been thirty-five years since he had rushed into a dingy recording room in Chicago to make his first record. It was Paramount Records then; he had played second guitar behind old Blind Joel Taggart. Tonight he was the guitar and voice for Mercury Records. They wanted to call this record "The Beginning."

Beginning, Joshua Daniel White thought. They can't kill me yet. I always come back for another round after they think I'm knocked out. I never miss a gig. I'll probably cut my last side in a hospital room. He smiled tentatively, wishing he didn't feel so tired.

Josh White appeared to be all health, vigor and self-assurance. At forty-nine, he retained his nimble athlete's body. A mustard-colored shirt open at the collar revealed a sensual neck and throat that had made so many women think twice. Sleek olive trousers ran down to a pair of custom-made shoes. Gracefully, he strode the studio floor joking with his accompanists.

A swirl of cigarette smoke moved around his head. He coughed to clear his throat, then took another deep drag. He fingered the talisman of St. Christopher that hung at his neck. Exploring, he touched the guitar strings. His lighted cigarette was parked straight up behind his right ear. Never burned yet . . . by cigarettes. He tried a half-voice run-through, just singing to himself. Josh White is the total actor, a showman in his sleep. He threw his head back and laughed uproariously. He closed his eyes, pursed his lips, pushed the words through. The session might work.

Herb Brown began to grunt a little run on his bass. Floyd Morris picked up the pulse on the piano with a few relaxed, bluesy chords and Eddie Williams brushed lightly on the snare. Gnarled, weather-beaten Sonny Boy Williamson kissed his harmonica affectionately and a piercing high yelp answered his kiss. The quartet looked to the man with the guitar for a cue.

He raised his right hand and school was in session. His fingernails were sore and breaking off, but not many people knew that. His fingers landed gently but decisively on the strings.

> "In the evening, in the evening,
> Baby, when the sun goes down,
> Lord, ain't it lonesome, ain't it lonesome,
> When your lover can't be found,
> When the sun goes down."

A stinging dart of sound came from the steel strings. "My guitar is my baby. It's another voice. It does what I want it to do." The guitarist's two voices arced the phrases of the old blues song leisurely. Love, loneliness and sinking suns were his stock in trade. Maybe his voice was not as urgent or passionate as it had been thirty-five years ago, nor as wine-velvet smooth as it was twenty years ago. No matter, for the years had their worth. He knew what it was all about now.

It was rough and painful to sing that night. "The doctor had told me to cancel the session and go to bed, alone. Hell, they've been telling me to rest since I was born. Seems I'm always fighting doctors, lawyers, A & R men, whites and Negroes. Maybe it's just me I've been fighting. It's like the Moor in 'Othello' after he killed Desdemona. The Moor says, 'I've done some good and they know it.' But I say I've done some good and I know it."

Josh White has told more people about the blues than almost any singer. He has been the moralist, preaching the musical gospel of democracy and decency. At almost the same moment, he has been the immoralist, the devil's advocate, talking about the pleasures of the flesh. He sired a whole style of performing in cabarets.

He left the South but the South never left him. He is still a Negro boy on the run. For every smile and hug there is anger and pain behind the mask.

Did they know what he was, when even *he* wasn't sure? More lives than one. Always in the ring, fighting for dough, fighting debt. Fighting the Right and then the Left. Should anybody have to fight all his life?

Joshua Daniel White, Southern boy on the run, friend of the Roosevelts and Scandinavian royalty, veteran musician, roustabout, heller, father, grandfather, idol, sinner, lover, teacher. Above all, a fighter. He moves with the style and grace of the pugilist and thinks of life as the opposition of two forces: them against me.

He is both the proudest product of the culture of the American nightclub and the most pained victim of the culture he helped to create. His story is a drama of violence alternating with tenderness. A self-made man constantly altering the pattern from which he sprung. A natural musician who found the world a boxing ring in which he has traded punches for half a century.

As the session continued, Josh thought about all the friends he'd made, the millions of people he'd sung to but never met. Not sure what he thought of himself, he was less sure what they thought of him today. What would they say about him?

One said: *"Josh White is a sensual man, an intense man of new experiences. A lot of what is in Josh is screaming out through his fingertips. A man of real personal physical courage."*

Said another: *"One of the kindest people in show business. You can't help liking him."*

Still another: *"Fascinating guy. Slips in and out of reality very readily. Improvises stories like songs. I like him."*

A musician: *"Impeccable ear. One of the greatest natural musicians I've ever heard. But folk musicians are a fanciful lot. They have to embroider their stories and tales so that they can give them the freshness of a new performance. He couldn't tell a lie, he's just a folk artist."*

A lawyer: *"Josh has a tremendous capacity for friendship and warmth. He's always been unsophisticated politically. Basically, he's an equalitarian with deep feelings about the Negro in the South."*

A radio personality: *"A good man, a man of integrity with an enormous burden of guilt since he went to Washington and genuflected."*

A song writer: *"One of the greats. He and Burl Ives and Richard Dyer-Bennet were the biggest guys of the Forties. We wouldn't have folk music all around today without Josh's contributions."*

A folklorist: *"Over-sophisticated. Over-refined. Lost his roots. Too commercial."*

A nightclub owner: *"Josh is a determined professional, with a sense of responsibility to the audience that almost puts him in another era. His public face, although apologetic, is one of enormous presence and strength."*

In 1947, Woody Guthrie wrote:
"Josh White, thanks to his early days as a boxer, is today more of a fighter than most of the other progressive folk singers. Josh, being a Negro, being a boxer, and being a sort of a genius at performing, holds his place in my

thoughts as a good example of a fighting artist with a message, with a big mass following and with that easygoing kind of a warm feeling that he draws from being a daddy of four kids, the husband of a woman who is wide awake to the fight the Negroes must put up to walk on ahead . . . . Josh is not always as rough, hard, as tough as I'd like to see him, nor does he always sing songs that interest me, but he does seem to hold the crowds everywhere he walks and sings with his guitar."

2- Cabaret King

Josh White took the 'Cellar Tavern' Route, the kind
of a route that would cramp my tailbone into wild
epileptic knots and fits, but Josh would feel just
as hog-tied and hobbled in my Guerilla Territory as I
feel around his drawing room and parlor crowds.
Woody Guthrie, "Singing High Balladryee"

THE BOTTLE of Cutty Sark was finished and so was the recording session. Rehearsal, run-through, playback, discussion, occasionally a clash. "Let's go with the third take. That's what it is." Josh was sung out for the evening. These hadn't been his standards like "One Meat Ball" or "Strange Fruit" or "Sam Hall" or "Jelly, Jelly." These had demanded a dredging of his memory, back to the late Twenties and early Thirties. Fine work on "Job: 19" and "Evil-Hearted Man." Another two sessions and they'd have a great record in the "can."

Josh drew tight the belt of his green leather topcoat. "Sonny," he said to the whimsical old harmonica man, "I've learned a lot from you tonight." Sonny smiled and invited him to his little rhythm and blues club on West Lake Street. Josh said he'd try to make it later. Sonny went off to play at a dilapidated saloon for a handful of tired Negroes under the "El" near

Western Avenue. Josh's first stop was his home base in Chicago, the Gate of Horn.

When young Josh arrived for the first time in Chicago in 1924, he was the ragged leader of Blind John Henry Arnold. The winter bit ferociously at Josh's bare hands as he beat a tambourine, the same tambourine he had been beating as he walked from Greenville, South Carolina, to Chicago. He didn't have a penny in his pocket.

Chicago in 1963 was another story. When the champ left the studio ring, his entourage surrounded him. Len Rosenfeld, his manager—quiet, understanding, painstakingly patient—was there. Terry Mehegan, his secretary, had flown in from New York. Dave Olson, a Chicago disc jockey and promotion man, was there. So was Alan Ribback, then operator of the Gate of Horn and A & R man of the recording session. Now, thirty-nine years later, Josh had arrived in Chicago in his Lincoln Continental. He was a star reputedly earning $100,000 a year.

Josh and his troupe walked three blocks to the Gate of Horn, a temple of night life. He entered the dimly lighted club with a swagger and smile for everyone. The bartenders waved as if it were some triumphal return. With both hands extended at once, he shook hands with two musicians. "Hey, mother, how the hell are ya?" he asked one of them. They asked how the session went, and he replied in mock concern, "Oy, Vey!" Josh ordered a favorite drink, a White Spider—two shots of vodka with a dash of peppermint schnapps. Tourists watched the party with ogle-eyes.

Josh smiled to everyone. But his friends knew he was worried about a sore throat. They knew he had heard the night before that his eighty-one-year-old mother had suffered a stroke in Greenville. They knew the more he worried the broader his smile.

"I'm not a folk singer, I'm a story teller. I don't pretend to be a singer. I'm thinking about the story because I must believe the story." He talked about the importance of diction—"What good are the words if the people don't understand them?" "Now that Leadbelly and Big Bill [Broonzy] are dead, I'm the granddaddy." He tried to figure out why Negroes never listened to him. "I never in my life been a 'Youssah, boss' or an Uncle Tom." He told of what a lousy place Greenville had been. "I never had a childhood," he said.

The champ's associates swirled around him. He could trust them to stay close. He needed and really liked them.

Upstairs at the Gate of Horn, Oscar Brown, Jr., was singing to tumultuous applause. "When I hear him, I feel like a has-been," Josh confided. Yet to Oscar Brown, Josh was no has-been.

"I first saw Josh fifteen years ago at Orchestra Hall. He was all alone then and powerful. I've learned a helluva lot from Josh, in form and content. He pointed the way to a lot of strong material and how to present it. Josh blazed the trail for Harry Belafonte and for me. Cannonball Adderley and I were talking just the other night about how the guy who pioneers is not always the guy to reap the richest dividends."

On stage or off, Josh is the king of the nightclub. It is the home of instant approval, where he basks in the limelight of a friendly audience.

"His art has flourished in the nightclub," says Win Stracke of the Old Town School of Folk Music in Chicago. *"His style has a built-in insistence. In the dark rooms of the cabaret, Josh is a virtuoso."*

13

Josh provides cabaret denizens the "kicks" they want with their liquor. He also makes them think a little about ethics and decency to people, all people. His guitar strings whine like a woman in ecstasy. Josh draws in his breath between his teeth with a sensual sound. Then he turns around and gives a musical sermon on democracy.

He thought about those thirty-five years. All those women. And all those women people thought he had. And those mean blind bastards who kicked him around. And "strange fruit hanging on the poplar trees," when he was only eight down South. Brass knuckles of the "Shakespeare Gang" on Chicago's West Side. The smear against him and the attempt to bury the smear that wouldn't stay buried. Oh, if he could have the money he had spent on doctors.

European royalty and the Roosevelts. Fast cars across the country. The time in Los Angeles when he and Murray Roman, the comic, ordered a tableful of "Black Sambo Pancakes" to teach a restaurant manager about Jim Crow. The kids after college concerts who wanted to know how he played overhand guitar, how he made those strings ring out, why he never used finger-picks like the others even though his nails hurt until he was miserable.

The Gate of Horn bar was noisy now but Josh White was lost in his own private world of recollection. What is it like to be a Negro in America? I'll tell them how lousy and how great it is. The five kids he raised in five rooms. The time he almost lost three fingers of his right hand, then almost lost his leg. The desperate desire to "fit in," to be loved and accepted. Why couldn't he ever really find peace and quiet in this world, except with the songs that stilled his listeners to a hush? Was he born unhappy in Greenville? Or was Greenville just an unhappy town to be born in?

14

3- I Never Had a Childhood

*B stands for the Blues
and M stands for Misery.*

"Blues Comes From Texas"

SULLIVAN'S ALLEY is grey and cramped. The little thoroughfare in the Negro ghetto of Greenville, South Carolina, has the smell of poverty about it. Poverty and hopelessness. There, as in slums throughout the South, an oppressed people tries to live out their lives with whatever dignity they can muster.

Joshua Daniel White was born on February 11, 1914, and given over to God. The house of the Rev. Dennis and Daisy Elizabeth White had the scent of poverty wiped clean with the astringent soap of piety.

"My daddy was a minister and my mother, well, she was very religious. The whole family was very religious. Till I was seven years old I had a boyhood. But after that I wasn't a child any more. I remember coming home from Southern Street school—you could just jump a fence to get to school. If we went the long way we had to go up one block, down one block, down one alley, then you were home."

Josh went only as far as the sixth grade. Before he left school he got whippings for such "sinful" conduct as puffing on a cigarette.

"We couldn't do anything at home, for fear of the Lord. We weren't allowed to drink soda water like orange soda, cherry, root beer. Grits we had every day. Couldn't even shoot marbles. At mealtime there was a long prayer. Everyone got on his knees and my daddy or my mama would pray ten, fifteen minutes. Then you'd get up and recite a different Bible verse at every meal. "What makes me tick? We were poor people, but always clean. When daddy wasn't preaching, he had a wagon and a steel-grey work horse. My daddy was a learned man and I have never seen him come to the table other than in a tie and collar. I have never heard my mother address my father other than Mr. White or papa address mama other than Mrs. White. When people

came into the house, men especially, they removed their hat. There is an old saying that enough is enough and too much stinks.

"I think you can be too religious. I know you can be too sinful. But at times you have to have some recreation. I know that we couldn't sing anything other than spirituals—they didn't say gospel in those days. There were no movies. There were no ball games. Dances were out. I've never seen anything in my house except buttermilk, milk and water."

Into this home one day walked a stranger who was to unleash a nightmare of savagery. He was a bill collector.

"The man had his hat on and papa said to him: 'Would you please respect my house—remove your hat.' Well, the man had heard but he acted like he didn't hear. He had a wad of snuff in his mouth. We had no rug on the floor but it was clean. Papa said: 'Would you respect my wife and children and remove your hat, please?' The man still didn't acknowledge it and he spit into the fireplace. But he missed and the wad of spit went on the floor. My daddy got the man—he was over six feet tall—by the scruff of the neck and put him out the door but didn't hit him. Maybe an hour later they came and took papa to the jailhouse. A day or two later this matron comes down to my mama and says: 'If you want to see your rooster, you'd better come up to the jail.'

"We went in the door, which was gated, and there was a long corridor with cells in the back which you couldn't see. The chief of police was called Big Chief Noe. He was about 280. The chief and another policeman hit my daddy. As he was falling down, my daddy grabbed Noe and I saw my daddy beaten to a pulp. I was about nine years old then, maybe ten. I promised myself I would kill Chief Noe, but someone beat me to it.

"My daddy was sent to the asylum, stayed there and escaped and came back home, when we were living on Jenkins Street. He never bothered anybody but they thought my daddy was crazy so they came back and caught him and sent him back to the asylum. He was bothering nobody. My daddy died in the asylum, I would say from the beating. I can remember the funeral parlor, brushing his hair, fixing his mustache just right and fixing his tie."

Into this world came tapping the cane of Blind Man Arnold.

"I met a blind man trying to cross a street named John Henry Arnold. We called him Big Man Arnold. When I say big, I mean like 260 or 270 pounds. He could take two bushels of grained corn and throw them over his shoulder either way. He asked me my name and then played me 'Joshua Fit the Battle of Jericho.'"

Man Arnold was to take Josh into a larger world, with more violence and suffering as its theme. A man of cruelty and avarice, he sang only religious songs. He could scarcely play the guitar, just frammed it with three or four chords. But he had a soaring, powerful voice, and Josh says the people believed whatever he sang. He tapped his way along with his daughter, Willie May, who played the tambourine for him.

Man Arnold said he wanted Josh for his lead boy, but permission from the stern old matriarch had to be obtained.

16

*"I asked mama and she said she would have to pray over it. I've said to peo-
ple she prayed for three days, but it was longer than that. God must answer my mother...she waited for an answer. If He doesn't answer, nothing
happens. Finally, the message came from the Man above. When Mr. Arnold
came back, mama said yes. I could lead him after school.*

*"When I was christened Joshua Daniel, my parents hoped I'd be something
great in the eyesight of the Lord. I thought that being the eyes of the blind
was something great in the eyesight of the Lord, because I remembered what
I had been taught about Joshua in the Bible. I thought how could I be anything great like Joshua? I'd have to grow up first. I'm still a baby, a child,
and I thought this was a step toward being something great in the eyes of
the Lord. My mother was promised $4 a week, which in those days was a
lot of money. And I left after that semester of school."*

At the age of about eight, Josh left Greenville. Hard-luck town. He
never had any luck in that town. Arnold left Willie May in Greenville, and he
and Josh went from city to city, heading South. When the sun went down in
the evening, Josh would lead Arnold off the shoulder of the highway, seek-
ing a dry place in the fields. One night, at a roadside, Josh was to see something that made him wish he had been blind, too. He never forgot what he
saw for the rest of his life.

*"I led Mr. Arnold over to the side of the road and we went to sleep. Out of
nowhere, I was awakened by a hand put over my mouth. It was like being
smothered, but then I heard a voice in my ear. "Joshua, don't be afraid, this
is Mr. Arnold." Then he stopped holding my mouth. As I started to wake
up, I began to hear a sound. Then my eyes got adjusted to what was around
me, and I saw where the noise was coming from. It was only as far as across
the street. There was a crowd of people stirring about and they had a bon-
fire.*

*"There were kids and adults. Drinking, a lot of drinking. Cider and white
lightning. Then I saw this—there were two figures. They were stripped
other than their shirts. Like on tiptoe. I don't think I could see them dan-
gling, but what I could see and what I can't get out of my eyes: I saw kids,
ten, twelve years old, girls and boys my age, mothers, fathers, aunts, adults
...the kids had pokers and they'd get them red hot and...and...it was
a hell of a thing to see. I came close to screaming but Mr. Arnold could sense,
as I was telling him what was happening, when I might scream and he
would put his hand over my mouth. How can you teach young children?
Mutilation. Torture. They must have been dead. The people were laughing.*

*"I never read anything about what happened or why. There is no why be-
cause this sort of thing never should happen. That's why I sing 'Strange
Fruit,' 'cause I know what I'm singing about.*

*"Mr. Arnold and I were afraid to leave until the mob left. It was not quite
dawn. They wouldn't wait 'till it got light for anyone to see what was happening. The mob vanished. We were just a few miles from Waycross, Georgia.
We were going there, but we turned back in the direction from which we
came.*

*"I don't call this childhood. I never had the childhood I wanted. Like having
skates or a sled or what kids would have in those days. I never had a toy
because I've worked all my life."*

4 - Dark Was The Day

Nobody cares for me,
Nobody cares for me,
'Cause I lost my sight and I have to be led,
Nobody cares for me.

It's so hard to have to be blind, Lord,
It's so hard to have to be blind, Lord,
I'm away in the dark and got to feel my way,
It's so hard to have to be blind.

I moaned the day I went blind,
I moaned the day I went blind,
Oh Lord, tell me how long. Am I to be blind always?
                        The Rev. Gary Davis

THERE WASN'T much that a blind Negro in the South could do but beg or sing. Disease and accidents left a high incidence of blindness among the Negro population. The blind street singer, from his curbstone pulpit or cobblestone stage, has been a legendary figure of the Southland, like generations of Homers before him. Out of his singing has grown a whole musical genre.

In most cases the blind bards divided sacred and sinful songs as sharply as the real-life gulf between spirit and flesh. But whether the lyrics told of worldly plaints or heavenly promises, the guitar backing and musical format were generally the same as the blues. So evolved the religious singers called the "holy blues men."

Josh White was to know both sides of the blind man's musical life —the "sinful" blues and sacred spiritual singing. John Henry Arnold was a religious singer of great power and persuasion. Josh would precede him, letting the singer hold his arm or shoulder. Setting up a curbstone church in town, Arnold would roar out the venerable spirituals. Coins were dropped into Josh's tambourine as he begged for Man Arnold, and the blind man with his unerring sense of pitch could discern just how many coins were in the tambourine. Although Arnold made enough money (sometimes $100 to $125 a weekend) and owned several racing horses, he would often deny his lead boy even an ice cream cone.

Josh recalls that Arnold was "mean, honest mean." Blind Joel Taggart was "tricky, nasty mean, and not really blind at all. He had cataracts and could see a little."

"Blind people I met were really hard. I should hate them for what they did to me but I don't. But really, I wouldn't give a blind man a penny now."

After the lynching near Waycross, Arnold and Josh made their way to Jacksonville, Florida. There, in the heart of the Negro section, Josh was to work for Arnold and three other blind men who were all singing together. After about three days, Josh was picked up by the police and taken off to jail.

"I'll tell you something: the majority of Negroes in the South, they were afraid of anybody in a blue suit or a uniform with brass buttons. As I went into the jail the captain called, 'Hey, nigger boy, come here.' He had a wooden blackjack and shoved it into my gut and I started getting sick and he said, 'Nigger, clean it up.' I didn't have a handkerchief and I was trying to clean it up with my hands. The cop behind me tore off my shirt to clean it up with. They kept me in jail four days till they had heard from my mother. They had arrested me 'cause they thought I had run away from home. I was eight years old."

As a boy, Josh was arrogant, but he was proud. While purchasing some Blue Ribbon snuff and Brown Mule chewing tobacco for Arnold in Jacksonville, Josh remembered to go to the back of the store but "forgot" to say "sir" and forgot he was wearing a skullcap that custom demanded he remove. "All of a sudden I was hit on the back of the head and my cap went sailing and as I stepped to pick it up—you know what a drop kick is? That's how I was used." Josh was kicked unconscious and suffered his injury for a month in painful silence.

Other blind men followed over the years. Blind Joe Walker was to be a major musical influence on Josh, as was Archie Jackson. Jackson fashioned his finger picks from the metal of sardine cans, giving his guitar playing a strong metallic clang that would carry the sound far. The most renowned blind singer of all was the immortal Blind Lemon Jefferson, a "sinful" blues singer from east Texas. Josh's memory is vague about the exact dates of their association, but he recalls he was about nine when he first met Lemon in Asheville, North Carolina. Josh says he led Lemon from time to time over a period of a year and a half through the major cities of North Carolina. Although Josh thinks of Lemon as the warmest and kindest blues singer he ever led, he does not remember the time as being a particularly happy one since he still "belonged" to Arnold who continued the practice of leasing him out to other blind singers. It was with Man Arnold that Josh traveled to Chicago in the winter of 1924. The boy of ten beat the tambourine with chill-swollen knuckles.

"I couldn't wear gloves beating the tambourine. Sometimes I'd get the spirit and I'd beat so hard I'd break the head and have to beat the rim. I'd get so cold I'd ask if I could go into a store and warm my hands and write to mama and tell her I was sick for a week. My mother didn't know what was happening to me. I didn't do this because I wanted to be with Arnold and I knew the money was needed at home. Finally, I left Arnold and went with a man named Joel Taggart who I thought was blind. I had met him in Greenville."

Taggart did only spirituals on the street, but at some of the house parties he played a mixture of blues and spirituals, getting $6 to $8 a night. Taggart revealed he was not blind when Josh surprised him rewriting a letter Josh had written his mother. Again Josh felt the need to escape.

The years in Chicago were recalled recently by a former employee of Paramount Records:

"It was possibly 1927 when I first met Josh White. He was brought to Paramount's Chicago office by Joel Taggart, a blind beggar. Josh was recording with Taggart. However, he wasn't receiving any money for those recordings. Mayo Williams paid Taggart and more than likely assumed Taggart was in turn paying Josh. I was horrified when Josh mentioned he was not allowed to go to school because Taggart traveled around so much. ["While we were in a city making money I would go to school," Josh recalls. "Then the money slacked off and we'd move to another city, every one or two months. But every time you'd go back a grade until they found out what you knew and by that time we'd be off again. That's why I had no schooling. Sixth grade is nothing."] *Josh loathed the idea of being forced to appear in clothing that was literally rags in order to get the sympathy of the public. I told Taggart to either let Josh go to school or send him back home, or I would report him to the authorities. He promised to see to it that Josh attended school.*

"After Josh broke with Taggart there was a problem of where he would live. My mother had agreed to let Blind Blake stay at her house while he was recording in Chicago. I asked Blind Blake if he would share his room with Josh and he agreed. [Josh recalls, however, living with his cousin Marie Miles until he left Chicago.] *As a young boy, Josh had impeccable manners. He was considerate at all times, and seemed to be congenitally nice and decent.*

"After that, Josh recorded frequently, with just about everybody. At the end of the summer he came to the Paramount office in a new suit. He told me he had saved some money and was going home to his mother."

5- Trouble and Triumph

Well, I've always been in trouble,
'Cause I'm a black-skinned man . . .
"Trouble," as sung by Josh White

I N HIS new suit, Josh White returned home in 1928. Greenville was still bad news. Even when he played a harmless game of football he was hounded by trouble. A broken leg landed Josh in the city hospital. The leg did not heal properly and the doctors had to break it again.

But there were consolations: "The nurses took a liking to me at the time," Josh remembers with a broad grin. "I was big enough." While he was recuperating, two men, W. R. Callaway and Art Satherly, talent scouts for the American Recording Company, found him.

As Satherly recalls the first encounter:

"Josh was recovering at the time from an illness and was very weak and thin. [Josh remembers being in a wheelchair, his leg in a cast.] He was in this little wooden unpainted house by the side of the road. In the little fireplace were a few smoldering embers giving off very little heat. There was no spare wood. "Josh was covered with a blanket and sitting in a chair. At that time he insisted that if he could record for American he would follow the advice of his mama and daddy and sing 'Christian' songs only. I asked Mr. Callaway to go to the store and get anything that Josh needed.
"About July of 1931, I contacted Josh again and brought him into New York for a recording. He was wonderful to work with and made recordings of 'Christian' songs and later, blues. When his first recordings were issued he was known as Joshua White, the Singing Christian."

The piety of Josh's parents followed him to New York. His first recordings, on the Perfect label, were of blues under his own name. But this caused a stir at home. Mama had said, "Don't sing any reels," and that included anything but spirituals. Josh remembers singing twenty-eight songs on three dates for which his mother received $100. Fifteen sides were issued in 1932. Among the songs were "Howling Wolf Blues," "Black and Evil Blues," "Baby, Won't You Doodle-Doo-Doo," "Depression Blues" and "Greenville Sheik."

To avoid family trouble, "Greenville Sheik" was the first of many recordings made from the early Thirties under the sobriquet of Pinewood Tom. Yet when Josh recorded "Christian" songs such as "Pure Religion Hallilu," "There's a Man Going Around Taking Names" and "I Don't Intend to Die in Egypt Land," he was called Joshua White, the Singing Christian.

The reputations of the Singing Christian and Pinewood Tom were growing throughout the Negro market. For a time the violence and poverty of Greenville seemed a memory to Josh. He started to appear on a National Broadcasting Company series called "Harlem Fantasy." The weekly show, conducted by Julian Street, Jr., featured such Negro talent as Clarence Williams, Eva Taylor and the Southernaires. For seven or eight months Josh was a fixture on the show. Then, trouble.

Somehow, even in New York, Josh could not leave the violence of the South behind him. Beneath the surface smile, Josh White was an angry man. His temper exploded one night in New York and he put his fist through a glass door. Rushed to the hospital, there was a danger the guitarist would lose his charmed right hand. For three years there was a constant threat of amputation. His hand remained paralyzed for five years.

One day in 1933 he met Carol Carr, a lovely young singer, at the Epworth Baptist Church in the Bronx. Carol's mother was captivated by "this nice, church-going boy from the South." Soon, Josh was charmed by Mrs. Carr's shy, philosophically patient daughter. He would walk two miles in the cold weather to see her. On Carol's birthday, December 23, 1934, they were married.

Once, Josh had to return to Greenville to bury an aunt. He arrived at the Southern depot and forgot for a moment that Negroes in that town don't ride in certain taxicabs and that there was "the walking tax." A plain-clothes detective tapped Josh on the shoulder and asked him for his permit. The police booked him for non-payment of his "walking tax," a sum of $87.23, which had to be paid under penalty of jail. Josh paid the fine, but never attended his aunt's funeral.

That week-end at a football game, Josh got into a fight. Unfortunately, one of the men he hit was a plainclothesman. Four officers subdued Josh, then grilled him. Why was he in town? Why were his hands so soft? They threw him in a jail cell with three convicted murderers. A call went out to old family friends, the Mauldins, an influential white family in Greenville.

One of the convicts said to Josh, "You get up on the top bunk. They're going to come and beat you." A few minutes later, three guards with their shirtsleeves rolled up entered the cell. In their hands were rubber hoses. "If I went down from the bunk, I knew I would get beaten up." The three condemned cellmates formed a phalanx between Josh and the guards. They said to the guards defiantly: "We're going to die anyway. You're not going to touch the Singing Christian." During the moments of hesitation, a call came through from the Mauldins and the police decided to let the "troublemaker" out of jail. He vowed to leave Greenville for good and told his mother of his plan to marry Carol. She gave him her blessing.

Back in New York, music work was slight for Josh. For his injured right hand, his mother sent him a plaster she made out of South Carolina red clay mixed with vinegar. To keep his new household together, he worked as a longshoreman for a packing and warehouse concern.

An opportunity to provide a home for Carol and his mother-in-law presented itself. Josh took a job as superintendent of a building in return for a four-room apartment in the basement. Later his brother, Billy, joined them. The round-the-clock job paid Josh and Billy $45 a month for their work, while Carol and her mother each made $25. Josh joined a janitors' union, but got into increasing difficulties with the building management for his "uppitiness." Josh maintains that the management wanted a kickback on his salary and feared his activity with the union.

He was discharged in 1937, and the slimmest days of the depression faced the family. Carol continued to work as a domestic, sometimes walking up five and a half flights of stairs, even while seven months pregnant. Josh's hand got worse. He had no references for a job. He finally went to work as a hotel operator. A house party here and there brought in a few dollars, but Josh remembers not being able to play very well then. Things were getting increasingly difficult and there were now two babies, Blondelle and Beverly, to care for. *John Henry* was to revive the career of Josh White and save his family.

6- John Henry

John Henry told his captain,
Says, "A man ain't nothin' but a man,
And before I'd let your steam drill beat me down, Lord,
I'd die with this hammer in my hand."

THE LATE Thirties in New York were a time of privation for Josh White and his growing family. The trouble with his hand had slowed his career, as had the general aura of the Depression that still gripped the country.

But by the beginning of the Nineteen Forties, Josh was to spiral out of semi-obscurity into national popularity. A major factor in this sharp change was his association with a show called *John Henry*. Although the musical failed, it called attention to the talents of Josh White.

Josh nearly missed being cast in the production because he was such a difficult man to find. Leonard de Paur, the arranger, choral director and jack-of-all-trades, was called in by Sam Byrd and Jacques Wolfe. They had a show, Roark Bradford's *John Henry,* about which they were very enthusiastic, but there were casting problems.

The producers wanted Paul Robeson to play the title role, but he was in Europe. There was another interesting part, called Blind Lemon—not the old east Texas blues singer, but more closely related to the "Greek chorus," who would stroll through the show doing an occasional musical commentary on the narrative. Who should do the part?

Roark Bradford and his wife had heard some of the early recordings by Joshua White, the Singing Christian, and they felt certain he was ideal. But de Paur had another candidate—a Southern blues man named Pinewood Tom, whom he too knew only from recordings. A lively debate ensued over the relative merits of Joshua White and Pinewood Tom. Shortly afterward they discovered that the two men were the same, and a year-long chase began to find Joshua-Pinewood.

At a New Year's Eve party, 1939, de Paur saw a young man at a table in the corner playing whist. On his lap was a guitar and over his ear was a lighted cigarette. After a play at the table, the musician would pick up his guitar and strum a blues verse:

"Well, you trumped my ace,
And I don't like your face."

De Paur listened to the commentary on the whist game and told himself this was just the person they wanted for *John Henry*. The music consultant asked the whist player what he did for a living, and the latter, not friendly enough to introduce himself, just said he ran an elevator. De Paur left the party, slightly quizzical. At 3 a.m. he called the hostess, Jean Cutler, and asked her the name of the elevator operator. "Why that's Joshua White." By 8 a.m. de Paur arrived at Josh's apartment. An immediate audition was arranged at Jacques Wolfe's house. The search was ended.

John Henry opened in December, 1939. After two weeks in Philadelphia and two in Boston, the show opened at the 44th Street Theatre. But, like many another Broadway casualty, *John Henry* closed in three weeks.

Out of the show, however, de Paur realized there was something to salvage in the singer who had played Blind Lemon, and he served as coach and arranger for a group that Josh brought together, later called the Carolinians. Josh was the featured singer. His brother, Billy, joined the group, as did Carrington Lewis, Bayard Rustin, later to become a political figure and writer, and the bass, Sam Gary.

After several months of rehearsal, the group went into a Columbia studio on June 4, 1940, to record an historic album called "Chain Gang." The album included "Chain Gang Bound," "Nine-Foot Shovel," "Trouble," "Told My Cap'n," "Going Home, Boys," "Crying Who: Crying You," and "Jerry, Lord, This Timber Got to Roll."

The session was conducted by John Hammond, whose long career in furthering Negro artists made him a giant in the field. He had known Josh since the days of the early Thirties when Josh recorded on the Perfect label.

The album was controversial from the outset. The Scottsboro Case was still recent and the newspapers were filled with extradition cases of fugitives from the chain gangs. A wave of compassion for the Negro was developing in the country. The abhorrence of Hitler's persecution of the Jews made America aware of its own worst problems, segregation and discrimination. Yet the true picture of the Negro life and suffering in the South had not been told. As has happened so often in American history, that story was best told by the music of the Negroes themselves.

Disputes over "Chain Gang" raged on every hand. Lawrence Gillert, who had released a collection of Negro protest songs, maintained that Josh had taken his material. Josh replied that he had known the songs for many years. But this quarrel was mild compared to the controversies within Columbia Records over the record's effect on Southern distributors. Some officials in Columbia wanted to hold up the release of "Chain Gang," but Hammond thought differently and fought for its release. The album won wide critical success and even sold in the South.

During this period Josh began to appear on a weekly radio folk music show on the Columbia Broadcasting System called "Back Where I Come From."

Hammond was determined to get Josh before as many listeners as possible. He introduced him to Barney Josephson, manager of the new club, Cafe Society Downtown. This began the period of widest recognition, 1940 to 1947.

24

7 — Cafe Society

Joshua White sings glad and sad
About a jillion good girls he ain't never had.
Woody Guthrie

CAFE SOCIETY did not cater to cafe society. The two Manhattan nightclubs bearing that name were cabarets for people who hated cabarets. By a skillful blending of talent, management and atmosphere, the two Cafe Society clubs managed by Barney Josephson were to leave their mark on the popular culture of the Nineteen Forties.

Cafe Society Downtown opened in 1938 in a low-ceilinged basement at One Sheridan Square, in a corner building where, to borrow H. Allen Smith's phrase, West Fourth Street and Washington Place come together like the legs of a man.

The downtown club was to become a focal point for people of a left-wing social orientation. Performers and patrons often viewed the world similarly. The temper of the times about Negro rights and the whole aura of post-Depression radicalism permeated the atmosphere.

Cafe Society was probably the first Manhattan club to systematically and consciously break down the color bar, seating Negroes without discrimination. The policy was pursued so zealously that it was once jokingly suggested that the best tables and best service went to Negro patrons.

Josh White was no intellectual, but he knew how to reach the intellectuals who frequented Cafe Society Downtown and Uptown. His ability to speak for and about Negroes through his music made his a dominant voice during the years of World War II. Many of the young ethnic purists of today's folk-music revival tend to dismiss Josh on stylistic grounds, not realizing that he helped to build the mass audience that today listens compassionately to Lightning Hopkins or Big Joe Williams.

Equally pioneering was the quality of entertainers that Josephson booked at the club. Cafe Society was to be the starting ground for such illustrious names in show business as Zero Mostel, Mildred Bailey, Hazel Scott, Billie Holiday, Jimmy Savo, Red Allen, J. C. Higginbotham and Josh White.

Josh first appeared at Cafe Society Downtown with the Carolinians in 1939. But the star of the group soon outstrode his ensemble. As a single, Josh started at $100 a week. By the time of his last engagement at the sister nightclubs in 1947 he was drawing $750 weekly and had become galvanically popular at the club, earning the applause of thousands.

At first, Barney Josephson undertook the role of informal adviser-cum-manager for Josh. He suggested that the singer start wearing the clothes that were to become his stage "costume"—slacks and an open-collar sport shirt.

And besides the "message" of equality, Josh began to project the frank sexuality that has been a cornerstone of his appeal. The dimly lighted Cafe Society Downtown was an ideal place in 1940 for such songs as "Jelly, Jelly," but he could still be singing the same song to a matinee audience of Vassar undergraduates in 1963.

Josh was nervous in his first solo appearance at Cafe Society Downtown. He was on a bill with the three great boogie-woogie pianists, Meade "Lux" Lewis, Albert Ammons and Pete Johnson. Also appearing that night were Red Allen, the trumpeter, and his combo.

"No one knew my name. And I had to be in the tail-end of the act. I told Barney, 'These people are here to eat and drink and socialize. They won't listen to me.' Barney didn't sympathize. He said, 'If you can't quiet them, you shouldn't be working here.'
"Barney, after introducing me, walked off the stage and I walked on. The noise in the place was terrible. I put my foot up on a chair. I smiled. They continued to talk. I started to tune the guitar, but they didn't listen. I started 'Evil-Hearted Man' without raising my voice one bit. I did about three verses and then it happened. They started to listen. They listened for years. It was the greatest goddam nightclub in the world."

It has been said that when Josh is stroking the strings of his guitar women feel as if he is stroking their bodies. The manner in which he sucks in his breath at meaningful moments, coupled with his vibrant good looks, all heighten the passion that Josh has been able to kindle in women, young and old.

But whether plying songs of sex, of racial consciousness or of such unabashed sentimentality as "Scarlet Ribbons" or "Molly Malone," Josh has an involvement with his audience that marks the trouper in the old vaudeville sense. Josh White sweats when he works, and you can't fake sweat.

The fame of the handsome young trouper at Cafe Society spread quickly. For three and a half years Josh was an institution at the club. There were occasional jobs at other clubs, such as the Village Vanguard and the Blue Angel. Richard Dyer-Bennet recalls his impressions of Josh at the Vanguard:

"I saw a good deal of Josh during the Nineteen Forties, heard him sing many times and worked on the same bill at the Vanguard. Leadbelly was on the same bill and Josh and Lead did some fine singing together. They complemented one another in a very satisfying way. Lead's voice and guitar were elemental, in a positive sense, bedrock, powerful, straightforward and essentially rural in style. Josh was subtler in sound, rhythm, inflection and essentially urban in character—though his roots were rural and gave him enough deep kinship with Lead to make them not incongruous as a duo. Lead was an old-fashioned man. Josh was a contemporary man. Lead gave the impression of power, gravity and rather serious, almost somber, purpose. Josh impressed me as having a lighter touch, quite a bit of levity, almost of light-hearted cynicism. Josh's performance manner was misleading and hid from many people the emotionally serious nature of his work."

For the many who never had heard Leadbelly or Big Bill Broonzy, Josh was to be *the* voice of Negro folk song. He could invest a song such as

"Strange Fruit" with enormous meaningfulness, even though it was not of the folk tradition. Billie Holiday had first sung the song about lynching and felt the song was "hers." Once, in a drunken rage, Josh says, Billie flashed a razor menacingly at him on the backstairs of the downtown club. Because he had "stolen" her song she wanted revenge, but Josh explained to her that "that song should be sung by everyone until it never had to be sung again."

Racial equality and sexuality were not only Josh's major themes on-stage. They became a way of life for him offstage during the Cafe Society days. Josh had his little prejudice "tests" for listeners at the Cafe. He would be invited to join them at their tables, then would take a drink from their glasses or a puff of their cigarettes when they were rested in ashtrays. If the patrons failed to return their glasses or cigarettes to their lips, Josh would know that some form of anti-Negro prejudice was stealthily at work, despite apparent friendship.

When it came to women, Josh was an ineluctable Don Juan. Some associates describe his aggressiveness with women as simply a pose, an "image" he felt compelled to maintain. Others knew better.

One man who knew Josh well during this period says: "Sex was 50 per cent of Josh's appeal."

Josh was involved in several fights during the Cafe Society days. He believes there was always a racial basis to the disputes, but others have felt it was his boldness with women that usually led to trouble.

Whatever the idiosyncracies Josh displayed in the years after the end of the war, they cannot obscure the great impact he had on the whole nation during the 1940 to 1947 period. It was an impact that had even taken him into the home of the first family in the nation, the home of the Roosevelts.

8—The Years of War and Peace

If you ask me, I think democracy is fine,
But I mean democracy without that color line.
Josh White's "Uncle Sam Says"

THE BIGGEST fight in Josh White's life was one he had to sit out from the sidelines. World War II found Josh, by then the father of four children, unable to serve in the armed forces. He decided to do his fighting at home; one enemy was still the same—prejudice against Negroes.

In 1941 Josh cut another disk that was to have a whiplash effect on the consciences of his listeners. For the Keynote label Josh recorded six songs under the title "Southern Exposure." One called "Uncle Sam Says" was written after visiting his brother Billy in an army camp. The album enjoyed a wide success and eventually was heard in the White House. As a result of the recording, President Franklin D. Roosevelt invited Josh to the capital.

"F.D.R. wanted me to sing for him. He had a whole room full of bigwigs, and Mrs. Roosevelt was there, too. I never thought of him as a polio victim until I saw him sitting there. I went up to shake his hand and he had that big grin on his face. His hand crunched mine like a bear. I pulled it back and said: 'Ouch, goddam it, I make my living with that hand.' The President laughed and said, 'Let's try it again.'
"Then I started to sing for him. Everything from the 'Southern Exposure' album—'Defense Factory Blues,' 'Hard Times Blues,' 'Bad Housing Blues,' 'Jim Crow Train' and particularly 'Uncle Sam Says.'"

The singer took especial delight in singing the verses to "Uncle Sam":

> "If you ask me, I think democracy is fine,
> But I mean democracy without that color line."

"Everything in those songs was true and Roosevelt was really interested. After the concert I spent about three hours in his chambers, singing, talking and drinking coffee royale—coffee and brandy. I told F.D.R. about the 'walking tax' in Greenville. He scarcely believed me. But I knew I was talking to Uncle Sam then and I had to tell him."

Josh was to be a frequent visitor at the White House and at the Roosevelts' country estate in Hyde Park, New York. Mrs. Roosevelt was to be the godmother of Donny (Josh Jr.) and Josh's brother, Billy, worked several years as Mrs. Roosevelt's chauffeur. Mrs. Roosevelt wrote about the family for an article in *Ebony* magazine:

"One of my younger friends is Josh White. I met Josh at a concert at which he was singing, and asked him if he would come to Hyde Park to sing at a Christmas party for the children from Wiltwyck School. I also invited his son, little Josh, because he sings, too. They both came and we became friends.
"Two of my best friends are Mrs. Alice Freeman and William White. They run my home at Hyde Park and I would be lost without them. Alice has been with me for fourteen years and, of course, I rely on her completely.
"My son told Josh that I was looking for a man to stay in the house as I did not think it a good idea for women to stay in the country without a man around the house. Josh surprised me by his answer. He said, 'I think my brother William would like to see your mother.' At first, I did not think William would like it too well. He had been in the entertainment world a long time with Josh, I knew. One day, without announcement, William appeared. We shook hands and he sat down and I interviewed him.
"I said to him: 'It will be very difficult for you to do housework, to drive a car.' William said, 'No, Mrs. Roosevelt, since the war, I don't feel like singing any more.' That was three years ago, and he has been with me ever since. I have an affectionate feeling for William, and I hope he has an affectionate feeling for me.
"Some of my Negro friends thought that I was creating what they call a social problem by having one brother as a rather requent guest and another broth-

er as a servant, more or less. I never saw that as a problem. Each has a dignified, necessary contribution to make.

"Sometimes, when Josh comes, William will come in and sing with his brother, but I always have to persuade him. Sometimes, I cannot persuade him, so Josh sings alone, unless Elliott or one of the other boys joins in.

"There are many times when Josh comes, and I don't know anything about it. He simply drops in to see his brother. Then he and William eat together. Sometimes, when Josh comes as a guest, he says, 'I'd rather eat with William.' And he does. Other times he eats with us, and William serves us. It seems most reasonable to me, and I have never had the slightest difficulty from the arrangement and never expect any. Perhaps that is because I never saw anything unusual in it."

Josh attended the Roosevelt Inaugural in 1945. He was becoming, by popular estimate, "The Presidential Minstrel" of the war years. As Josh recalls, President Roosevelt's favorite songs were "The Riddle Song," "Motherless Child" and "Beloved Comrade." Mrs. Roosevelt's were "The House I Live In," "Joe Hill" and "Dip Your Fingers in the Water." Having the President's ear and friendship was very important to Josh.

During the war years, Josh continued to work at Cafe Society Uptown and Downtown and at the Blue Angel. In 1942, he traveled to Mexico on a good will trip with the Golden Gate Quartet, a jaunt that enhanced the reputations of both. He appeared at many benefits for such groups as Bundles for Britain, Negro Rights and Yugoslav War Relief. Everyone who recalled those days now expresses the belief that Josh was basically an apolitical person who was courted by the Radical Left, including pro-communists, and undoubtedly used by them as well. The effects of the then-legal activity were not to be felt until 1950.

During the war years, Josh was to come into contact with many of the leading performers in America's entertainment world. Among his friends and acquaintances of that time were Josephine Premise, Edward G. Robinson, Canada Lee, Mary Lou Williams, Ethel Waters, Pete Seeger, Hazel Scott, Robert Preston and Lena Horne. Josh coached Harry Belafonte in blues styles on several occasions. Pearl Primus was in her heyday then and danced to many of Josh's songs. Among others with whom Josh worked were Eartha Kitt, Libby Holman and Burl Ives.

While there was a friendly relationship between Josh and Leadbelly, two more individualistic performers could scarcely be described. Josh had always been concerned about the niceties of diction. "What good is it if they can't understand what you're singing?" he asked the Louisiana singer on several occasions. Josh, too, was concerned that Leadbelly was always playing the clown for his audiences and told Leadbelly, "I wouldn't play the clown for my mother." Leadbelly replied: "I'm laughing at them. They're not laughing at me."

Josh was annoyed, too, that Leadbelly was allowed to walk around Manhattan with holes in his shoes. He found the disheveled and seemingly careless attitude of the king of the twelve-string guitar hard to fathom. However, he had enormous respect for the giant of folk song. When Huddie Ledbetter died in 1949, Josh was asked by Martha Ledbetter to sing "Precious Lord" at the funeral.

There were similar points of contact and great disparities in the relationship between Josh and Big Bill Broonzy. The biggest difference in blues style between Josh and Big Bill revolved around who was being pleased. Big

Bill is reputed to have said six months before he died, in 1953, that the only man left in America to play the blues after he died would be Josh.

In the mid-Forties Josh began his long association with Mary D. Chase, his manager, who was to play a pivotal role in getting work for Josh, advising him on his personal and professional life and helping the debt-ridden singer to manage his financial affairs.

The post-war world was to begin a new period for Josh White as it was for so many returning veterans and those who had stayed at home. There was still a lot of nightclub and concert work for him, but the golden days of Cafe Society were coming to an end. In 1950, he left with Mrs. Roosevelt for a triumphal tour of Scandinavia and Western Europe. The triumph was to be cut short, and Josh's life was to be irrevocably changed by the entry of his name in a publication called *Red Channels*.

9–The Albatross of Guilt

There's no hiding place down there,
There's no hiding place down there,
Oh I went to the rock to hide my face,
The rock cried out, 'No hiding place,'
There's no hiding place down there.
Traditional spiritual

A TIME OF tragic change in the life of Josh White struck in 1950. For his concern about decency among human beings in the Nineteen Thirties and Forties, he was to pay a heavy penalty. For his guilelessness in giving of his talents to those who asked for his help, he was to be hounded. Caught in the maelstrom of McCarthyism, Josh was to become a man victimized by the political Right and Left.

His "moment of truth" came in 1950. In June of that year Josh left for Europe with Mrs. Roosevelt, Elliott Roosevelt and others on a six-week tour. He was suffering from a cold when the plane left, and by arrival time he was running a fever and had burst an eardrum. In Oslo he was rushed to a hospital.

Recovering quickly, Josh started a round of triumphal concerts in Stockholm, Oslo and Copenhagen. The papers in Scandinavia hailed him as a protégé of Mrs. Roosevelt. He will never forget the tumultuous reception he received at the Tivoli Gardens in Copenhagen where an adoring audience listened through a drenching rain.

During this European swing, Josh had many requests for "Jim Crow Train" and "Strange Fruit." But he refused to sing these songs far from American shores, being reluctant to present this picture of American life. He explained to Europeans:

"We'll fight it out for ourselves. My mama and daddy taught me to clean out my own back yard. I'll sing everything in America, yet I won't sing everything in other countries. There is an extreme view here about 'lynching in Times Square,' and I simply won't cooperate with that view. I will sing my version of 'The House I Live In,' though. I don't make speeches, but I do sing."

The news that Josh had been listed in *Red Channels* for performing before alleged Communist-front groups came to him in London via telephone from Mary Chase.

The thunderbolt struck within weeks of his having sung at the American Embassy in Denmark where, "black tie" for the first time, he led King Augustus of Denmark and the other guests in singing "On Top of Old Smokey" and "When the Saints Go Marching In." The distance from triumph to tragedy was a trans-Atlantic plane flight.

Josh flew from London to Idlewild and was kept waiting for hours while customs officials telephoned Washington to find out if he should be sent to Ellis Island or permitted re-entry to the United States. The next day he spoke to two executives of *Red Channels,* the publication of Aware, a self-styled blacklisting group appointed to maintain the political "purity" of the entertainment and broadcasting industries. Of his talk at Aware, Josh says today:

"I said to these guys: Where did they get the lie that I was fronting for the Communist party? They said, 'You worked for Cafe Society, which was worked by the C.P.' They questioned me who was at what benefit and I tried to explain that it was impossible for me to remember. They tried to link me with the activities of Paul Robeson. I told them how and where I disagreed with Paul—he had said no Negro would fight against Russia. He couldn't speak for American Negroes any more than I could."

Two days later Josh was called to Aware, where he met Alvin W. Stokes, an investigator for the House Un-American Activities Committee. Josh said Stokes threatened him: "If you don't come down, we'll subpoena you down." Josh, enraged, at that moment decided to make a voluntary appearance before the committee and a statement was drawn up. "The guys at *Red Channels* said: 'We'll clear you if you attack Robeson.' I told them I didn't come to attack Robeson. I was there to squash a lie. I'm going to attack him? Crap. I'm not built that way."

The hearing of the House Un-American Activities Committee was like a star chamber. Because the actual testimony of Josh White has been so widely misinterpreted and vilified, the text of that statement is here given in full from the record of the committee:

Friday, September 1, 1950

UNITED STATES HOUSE OF REPRESENTATIVES,
Subcommittee of the Committee on Un-American Activities,
Washington, D.C.

PUBLIC HEARING

A subcommittee of the Committee on Un-American Activities met, pursuant to adjournment, at 10:15 a.m., in Room 226, Old House Office Building, Hon. John S. Wood (chairman) presiding.

Committee members present: Representatives John S. Wood (chairman), Francis E. Walter, John McSweeney (arriving as indicated), Richard M. Nixon (arriving as indicated), and Harold H. Velde (arriving as indicated).

Staff members present: Frank S. Tavenner, Jr., counsel; Louis J. Russell, senior investigator; Donald T. Appell, Courtney Owens, and Alvin W. Stokes, investigators; and A. S. Poore, editor.

MR. WOOD. The committee will be in order, please.

MR. TAVENNER. Mr. Chairman, there is a witness here who desires to appear voluntarily before the committee this morning, and I would like to call him, Mr. Josh White.

MR. WOOD. Hold up your right hand, please. You solemnly swear that the evidence you give this subcommittee shall be the truth, the whole truth, and nothing but the truth, so help you God?

MR. WHITE. I do.

MR. WOOD. Let the record disclose that for the purposes of this hearing a subcommittee has been set up by the chairman consisting of Mr. Walter, Mr. Velde and Mr. Wood. Mr. Walter and Mr. Wood are here. Mr. Velde will be here in a few minutes.

TESTIMONY OF JOSHUA DANIEL WHITE

MR. TAVENNER. Will you state your full name?

MR. WHITE. Joshua Daniel White.

MR. TAVENNER. When and where were you born?

MR. WHITE. Greenville, South Carolina, February 11, 1914.

MR. WOOD. Have you any objection to photographers making pictures?

MR. WHITE. That is quite all right.

MR. TAVENNER. What is your occupation?

MR. WIHTE. Singer, actor, and musician.

MR. TAVENNER. If you will speak a little louder, please. I believe you specialize in singing folk songs, do you not?

MR. WHITE. Yes.

MR. TAVENNER. How long have you been engaged in singing folk songs?

MR. WHITE. Since I was about seven years old.

MR. WOOD. For the record, who is the person accompanying the witness?

MR. STOKES. Mrs. White.

MR. TAVENNER. I believe you are accompanied by your wife rather than by counsel; is that right?

MR. WHITE. That is right.

MR. TAVENNER. You have expressed a desire to appear before the committee to make a statement with regard to your own activities?

MR. WHITE. That is right.

MR. TAVENNER. And I believe you have such a statement prepared, have you not?

MR. WHITE. I have.

MR. TAVENNER. I am going to suggest that you read it to the committee, and if you desire to add anything to it, that you do so, but before doing that I want to ask you, are you now or have you ever been a member of the Communist Party?

MR. WHITE. No.

MR. TAVENNER. You may proceed with such statement as you desire to make.

MR. WHITE. Thank you.

Mr. Chairman and members of the committee, I am here, as you know, quite voluntarily, and I want to thank you for this opportunity to clear up some misunderstandings about myself in some quarters. I have prepared this statement, which I shall read with your permission, after which I shall gladly answer any questions you may wish to put.

My conscience is clear. I intend to do some explaining for my own sake, and for the sake of many other entertainers who, like myself, have been used and exploited by people who give allegiance to a foreign power.

In recent years a lot of us have been drawn by our heartstrings into groups fixed up to look like noble causes which were later found to be subversive. I regret, and I suspect that many artists share the same deep regret with me, that an effective exposure of communistic activities in the theatrical and musical fields had not been made long before now.

Artists are not often smart about politics. We know mighty little about the ins and outs of "movements" and parties. But we're apt to have strong feelings and therefore are easy prey for anyone who appeals to our sense of justice and decency. Though it's not pleasant to talk about myself in public, I feel I owe it to my family and to other artists in the entertainment field to do so.

I have never knowingly belonged to or supported any organization designed to overthrow the Government of the United States. But I did on many occasions appear at benefits and rallies which I was led to believe were for worthwhile causes. I did not even suspect that some of them were Communist inspired. I did on some occasions sign petitions against lynching or poll tax or other evils.

(Hon. Harold H. Velde entered hearing room.)

MR. WHITE (continuing). Dozens of other artists of all races and colors, I have no doubt, have also given their names and talent and time under the innocent impression that they were on the side of charity and equality. Let me make it clear, if I can, that I am still on that side. The fact that Communists are exploiting grievances for their own purposes does not make those grievances any less real.

As I've said, I am no politician. On the other hand, I do know what injustice and discrimination and Jim-Crowism mean. I know these things not as theories but as cruel facts that I've seen and suffered in my own life. Against those things I have protested and will go on protesting, because I love my country and want to see it a better, more tolerant, place to live in. I'm proud of the fact that under our system of freedom everyone is able to speak out—or in my case, to sing out—against what we consider wrong and for what we consider right.

I am what is called a folk singer. I was a folk singer long before I knew what it is called. Even when I was a boy I made up and sang songs of ordinary people, trying to convey their joys and sorrows, their grievances and their hopes. In this, I was expressing not only my own sentiments but the feelings of humble people generally, whatever their color or their names.

A folk singer, it seems to me, is the voice and the conscience of his time and his audience. He tries to put into words and music what those around him feel. This I shall continue to do, with God's help, as long as there is suffering and discrimination around me and freedom and equality to be won.

But that's not Communism, even if Communists try to use us for their own foul ends. As I see it, it's simple Christianity. And I say this as the son of a minister brought up in a religious family. I say this as the father of four daughters and a son whom my wife and I are trying to bring up as patriotic and religious Americans—which is to say, as decent human beings.

I was seven years old when I left my home in Greenville, South Carolina, to help support myself and my family. My job was to lead a blind man while playing the tambourine. Before I was eight years old I knew what it meant to be kicked and abused. Before I was nine years old I had seen two lynchings. I got to hate Jim Crow for what it did to me personally and because Jim Crow is an insult to God's creatures and a violation of the Christian beliefs taught by my father.

That's how I became a folk singer. I discovered that I had some talent for putting together words and fitting them with tunes on my guitar. When I was about sixteen, a man from Chicago convinced my mother and father to let me record some songs. I recorded under the title, "Joshua White, the Singing Christian." My mother received $100 and no royalties for twenty-eight recordings. After that I went on the radio. Of course, I was thrilled by the career opening up for me—but I was even more thrilled by the chance to tell my fellow Americans, through my songs, about the wrongs that needed righting.

After that, I had some bad luck. I hurt my hand in an accident and for five years it remained paralyzed. Because I couldn't play, I felt as if I had been struck dumb. The doctors wanted to cut off three fingers, but I was stubborn—just hoped and prayed for a cure, meanwhile doing all kinds of jobs, running an elevator, anything, to keep alive. Then the paralysis ended. I got a role in a play, *John Henry,* in which Mr. Paul Robeson had the lead.

I have a great admiration for Mr. Robeson as an actor and great singer, and if what I read in the papers is true, I feel sad over the help he's been giving to people who despise America. He has a right to his own opinions, but when he, or anybody, pretends to talk for a whole race, he's kidding himself. His statement that the Negroes would not fight for their country, against Soviet Russia or any other enemy, is both wrong and an insult; because I stand ready to fight Russia or any enemy of America.

There are some Communists among Negroes, as I am told, just as there are among other Americans. But they don't speak for the rest of us, any more than white Communists speak for white Americans. I am told that the proportion of Negro members in the Communist fold is even smaller than the proportion of other races; and that says a lot for their common sense.

When Communists and their kind talk about "democracy" and "equality," they are using double talk. They use good words in their own topsy-turvy way, to cover up bad intentions. But for simple folk who don't know the art of turning words inside out, it takes time to catch on.

34

Anyhow, after *John Henry* I was pretty well launched. I made albums: the "Chain Gang" album by Josh White and His Carolinians, and another by myself I called "Southern Exposure." Gradually I began to rise in my profession.

At that point, I suppose, my name began to have some value for publicity purposes, to attract a crowd and raise money. All kinds of invitations came to me, and when they sounded right, I was happy to accept. Many times, between my professional shows, I'd go to perform where my only reward was the belief that I was helping some good cause. When I received invitations from men I trusted, or groups with fine-sounding titles and lists of prominent citizens on their letterheads, asking for my time or signature, I gladly agreed. Inside me I felt I was doing a little to extend the area of freedom in my native South and the world generally.

Looking back, I just wish someone had told me! Many of the organizations were genuine. Some others, as I learned the hard way, were phony, false-face political rackets, exploiting my eagerness to fight injustice. I didn't become aware of this, however, until about 1947.

I was in California at the time. In the newspapers I came across a list of committees and organizations which the Attorney General had just labeled "subversive." And I was horrified to learn that a number of them were organizations for whom I had performed in the course of years, without knowing their character.

It was an awful blow. I realized that I had been played for a sucker. There I was, a devoted American who had let himself be used.

I discussed the situation with my manager, Mary Chase, who took over my affairs in 1947. She was as distressed as myself. We decided to check on those invitations for benefits and rallies. More than that, we made contact with a New York newspaperman, Howard Rushmore, who knows a lot about the Communist rackets and could give us some guidance. Despite this, as I have discovered recently, I was again taken in or had my name used, without my permission, several times by the disguises. A few of them even advertised me without my knowing.

Permit me to quote from a letter I wrote to Mr. Rushmore almost two years ago, when it came to my attention that I was being charged with Communist sympathies. After denying the absurd charge, I wrote:

The love I have for America, the land of my birth, which has given me every opportunity, is far too great to permit of any other allegiance. . . . I have no interest in any particular party. I am solely devoted to the principle of a democracy like ours, that stands for the welfare of all its people regardless of race, creed or color.

My one consolation, as I think back to the many nights I gave to concealed subversive groups, is that I never sang anything I didn't believe. Often I sang the powerful song, "Strange Fruit," which is an indictment of the horror of lynching. But I always followed it with what I call the answer to "Strange Fruit"—"The House I Live In" or "What Is America to Me," which expressed the other side of the story—my profound love for our America.

Why shouldn't a Negro artist—and for that matter any decent person—raise his voice aginst lynching? Here's how the song, "Strange Fruit," goes:

Southern trees bear a strange fruit; blood on the leaves—
 and blood at the root.
Black bodies swinging in the southern breeze—
 strange fruit hanging on the poplar trees.
Pastoral scene of the gallant South,
 of the bulging eyes and the twisted mouth.
Scent of magnolias, sweet and fresh—
 and the sudden smell of burning flesh.
Here is a fruit for the crows to pluck,
 for the rain to gather, and for the wind to suck;
For the sun to rot, for the trees to drop.
Oh, here is a strange and bitter crop.

My records of this song have sold big. If they helped make my fellow Americans more aware of the evil, I am pleased. But then I would insist on also performing "The House I Live In," which seems to me to express the things for which all good Americans are ready to stake their lives if necessary. Here's how it goes:

What is America to me?
A name, a map, a flag I see,
A certain word, democracy.
What is America, to me?
The house I live in—a dream—that must come true,
A land of food and shelter—and there's work for all to do,
The right to earn a living
To make us really free,
Where everyone is working,
That's America to me.
The house I live in—the same for black and white,
My Country right or wrong—if it's wrong, to set it right,
A land where all are equal,
The house I want to see,
Where all will have four freedoms,
That's America to me.
The loved ones we remember—who fought that we might live,
The nameless unsung heroes—who gave all that one could give,
Defenders of our freedoms—the women and the men
Who love the house we live in
But won't come home again.
The house I live in to cherish and to love,
To make a worthy dwelling—in the image they dream of,
A welcome on the doorstep—for everyone to see,
And a window in the future,
That's America to me.

I believe that no one who sings such songs honestly, from the heart, can be a Communist. They're songs that put a high value on human life and on personal freedom. But the Communists don't consider those things important.

Some months ago I made a concert tour in Europe. I was both amazed and annoyed that somehow only one of my dozens of recordings was being circulated in those countries, namely "Strange Fruit." So wherever I appeared, the audiences requested me to sing it.

But I refused, and I told my audiences why. I tried to make them understand that America is the best and freest country in the world. It is the kind of democracy that makes it possible to fight injustice and achieve progress.

It's one thing to complain of lynching in America, where your listeners know that it does not detract from your loyalty and love for your country. It seemed to me quite another thing to complain of it abroad, where the listeners might think it's the whole story. Jim Crow and the rest of it, we all know, are on the decline. More and more Americans are ashamed of it and doing something about it. In any case, it's our family affair, to be solved by Americans in the peaceful, democratic American way.

In some of those European cities I was interviewed by reporters. There are the clippings to show that I spoke of my pride in our country, and denied the libel that my people would not fight and die to defend America.

In the midst of all this, I got news that I was being attacked back home as fronting for the Communists. Considering that I was doing the very opposite, that was quite a blow. So I cut short my tour in order to return and expose that lie. That, Mr. Chairman, is how I happen to be here today.

My entertainment for these subversive groups was innocent on my part, and is far in the past. I am concerned, however, for my wife and children. The very notion that their father and husband is partial to Communism has come to them as quite a shock. I want to reassure them on this score, in the open and without question.

About two years ago my boy, who was then seven and is very gifted musically, gave a concert in Chicago at Orchestra Hall. Among other things he sang "Marching Down Freedom Road," and that's a fine, rousing plea for true democracy. He also sang "The Lord's Prayer," one of his favorites, which he sings often in his Sunday School. But some paper, believe it or not, said the child was Communist. It took us some time to get over that insult.

Besides the family, I decided that I also have a duty to other folk singers and artists in general, especially young people just getting started. They face the same thing I did. I want my sad experience to stand as a warning to them. I hope they will give themselves to good causes as generously as I have tried to do. But I hope also they will be more careful who uses them and why. My advice to them is plain and clear: Be sure to look under the label.

Personally I have little to retract or regret, other than the auspices under which I have sometimes appeared. As long as my voice and spirit hold out, I shall keep on singing of the hope, joys, and grievances of ordinary folk. I shall stand shoulder to shoulder with those who are pushed around and humiliated and discriminated against, no matter what their race or their creed may be. That, as I see it, is the least I can do for the country we all cherish.

But those who would tear down our America, those who hold a double allegiance, those who turn words upside down and inside out in support of a foreign tyranny—they're my enemies. Better than most people in this room I know the blemishes on our American civilization. I think we should all devote ourselves to removing them, not merely because they give aid and comfort to the Communists, but because they're wrong in themselves.

I thank you.

MR. WOOD. Any further questions, Mr. Counsel?

MR. TAVENNER. Mr. Chairman, I believe I have no questions to ask.

MR. WOOD. Mr. Walter.

MR. WALTER. You have stated that had you known that some of those movements that you were assisting were Communist fronts, you would not have participated in their activities?

MR. WHITE. That is right.

MR. WALTER. I think by that statement you have made out a very strong case for the enactment of the Wood bill that the House just passed this week, because under the provisions of that law Communist-front organizations will become known.

MR. WHITE. I am glad.

MR. WALTER. And the names of these organizations and who supports them will become public property.

MR. WOOD. Mr. Velde.

MR. VELDE. No questions.

MR. WOOD. The committee appreciates your coming before us and making this contribution. I hope that others who have been similarly imposed upon by Communist-front organizations will wake up to that fact. We appreciate your presence here.

MR. WHITE. Thank you so much.

(*Whereupon the witness was excused.*)

The newspapers instinctively found the lead item for their story in the comments Josh had made about Robeson's statements that Negroes would not fight against the Soviet Union. Though he felt he had not in any sense attacked the baritone, the headlines interpreted his statement to the committee in that manner.

Having fenced off the Right, Josh now had to defend himself from the Left. At Cafe Society and the Vanguard the waiters didn't want to serve Josh. Yet, at the Black Orchid in Chicago, people called Josh White a Red. Others around the country shunned him for "cracking," for "playing ball," for "self-serving."

"So I was nowhere. Erasing my name out of Red Channels, *well, it has never happened. Yet I would do the same thing again. People said I went to Washington and called names, even though I didn't. I'm singing and will sing songs that are good for America. I'm out there trying. I don't believe in Uncle Tom."*

Josh maintains that his name in *Red Channels* triggered a personal blacklist that is plaguing him to this day. Although he was to get occasional jobs on television in the next dozen years, *Red Channels* and the attendant notoriety left a mark on Josh's career that time has been painfully slow in erasing. It is hard to measure whether more damage was done to his image by his having sung for some alleged Communist-front organizations or by his attempt to justify what he had done. From the Left came a sort of Coventry of silence, a chilling alienation because he "tried to clear himself."

The travail of Josh White has been one that scarred the whole nation. The Blacklist and the Investigation have driven men to suicide, have spread a sort of terror, forced "moments of truth" upon hundreds of former Communists, Leftists, Liberals and, like the singer, easygoing and politically unsophisticated persons who could not see the contact with Communists or pro-Communist groups as quite the evil that the radical Right portrayed it to be.

That Josh made a concession to the investigators and the blacklisters by his voluntary appearance is obvious. What is less widely known is that he did not turn informer, that he did not really attack his long-time friend, Paul Robeson. Instead, he tried to walk a tightrope of integrity.

Josh White's strength has never been that of a conventional sort. His is the sensitivity of a man who hates oppression. His ability to bear physical pain is not great. Worse, his ability to bear emotional pain or rejection is even less.

10 – The Comeback Trail

They whipp'd Him up and they whipped Him down,
What you going to do when your lamp burn down.
They whipped that man all over town,
What you going to do when your lamp burn down.

Traditional spiritual

JOSH WHITE was one of hundreds in the entertainment world who have been caught in the juggernaut of McCarthyism, the cruel vise between conscience and expediency, between duty and integrity, between the incredible economic threat of being blacklisted privately and vilified publicly. You never clear your name. People remember the accusation, not the reply to the accusation.

The comeback trail for Josh White has been long and rocky. Some said that Josh could never come back after Washington. But he was a born fighter and a born entertainer. The late Forties, when the private blacklisting had already started, and the early Fifties, were to mark many changes in Josh's career. It was not until the general folk-music revival of the mid-Nineteen Fifties that Josh was to end the stormiest part of his career and once more surge into popularity.

Josh's life in the theater and films was sporadic. It always had verged on the edge of success, but singing remained his chief method of expression. In May, 1945, Josh had appeared in *Blue Holiday,* an all-Negro variety show in which he co-starred with Ethel Waters. Transplanting much of the musical fare of his nightclub acts to the stage, Josh won rave reviews.

In February, 1948, Josh appeared in a play at Maxine Elliott's Theatre called *A Long Way from Home*. Josh was cast in the role of Joebuck, the angry crook. The play by Randolph Goodman and Walter Carroll was a translation of Gorki's *The Lower Depths* into the milieu of the American Negro. The frankly experimental play won respectful reviews.

As mentioned earlier, Josh's flirtations with Hollywood were brief and not altogether successful. In *Current Biography* of August, 1944, the following reference to his film career is made:

As a sensitive and proud member of his race, he refused not long ago to ac-cept lucrative motion-picture offers, too, because they were offers to play the conventional "Uncle Tom" parts usually accorded to Negro entertainers. At the time of his refusal, in fact, he had already had such an experience in Holly-wood, having made two full-length films which he now chooses to forget.

The two films were *The Walking Hills* and *Crimson Canary*. But the third in which he appeared is not easily forgotten: Hans Richter's *Dreams That Money Can Buy*. Reviewing the film in May, 1948, Bosley Crowther of *The New York Times* found the film generally too arty, but added:

This reviewer was most taken with a sequence which could fit very nicely into one of those familiar cartoon packages that Disney puts out. It's a cute-ly satiric animation in which two store-window dummies romance, to a John Latouche song which Libby Holman and Josh White sing, "The Girl With the Pre-fabricated Heart."

In late 1949, the theater beckoned again. In December of that year, both Josh and Josh Jr. appeared in *How Long Till Summer,* a play about the life of the Negro in a white world. The play by Sarett and Herbert Rud-ley was staged at The Playhouse for seven performances.

After the appearance in Washington, the lure of work in Britain was all the greater for Josh. The early Fifties were a time of near political exile for many who had formerly been aligned with the American Left. While Josh was never a political exile, the air in Britain was freer for him, both as a political victim and as a Negro.

British audiences were always enthusiastic for Josh and the critics would treat him with great respect. During appearances in Britain in 1950 and 1951, for instance, *The London Daily Express* praised Josh for "his deep, wine-velvet voice, which can convey sincerity, biting cynicism or bland im-pudence."

During 1950, Josh began a long series of programs for the British Broadcasting Corporation's Home Service. Working there with Charles Chil-ton, the producer, Josh's B.B.C. credits included a 45-minute life story of the singer from Greenville, South Carolina.

In 1951, Josh barnstormed through England and Scotland, doing as many as thirty concerts in thirty days. Again, illness plagued the singer. In February, 1951, Josh collapsed after a concert in Birmingham, England, with an infected foot. He was rushed 100 miles to Manchester for an opera-tion. Subsequently, Josh appeared in British concert and music halls with a heavily bandaged leg.

In 1953, Mary Chase died, but Josh continued to make his way with-out her invaluable aid and advice. In 1955, another pivotal year, he began his recording career with Elektra Records. Taken as a group, Josh's eight LP's on Elektra, made between 1955 and 1962, represent his best work on LP until he started the retrospective series of recordings on Mercury called "The Beginning." "The John Henry Story" and "Josh at Midnight" are con-sidered his best efforts on the Elektra label.

Meanwhile, Josh returned to Chicago and began a long association with the Gate of Horn. This companionable club, when run by Albert B. Grossman and then Alan Ribback, was to be Josh's primary performing milieu for a number of years. He helped put the famed San Francisco nitery, the hungry i, on the map, but a clash with its manager, Enrico Banducci, made that association brief.

In September, 1959, Josh returned to the site of an earlier triumph. In the room where Cafe Society Downtown had thrived, two Greenwich Village producers, Kelsey Marechal and Martin Lorin, opened a theatre-cabaret called One Sheridan Square. Josh was booked for ten days, and people were saying to the club's owners: "You're nuts. Josh's career is dead." Far from dead, Josh set all records for One Sheridan Square. Subsequent appearances at the Village Gate brought both generations of Josh fans, the girls of the Forties who were now the mink-coated matrons of the Sixties, and their children.

Television appearances in the Nineteen Fifties were rare for Josh. He maintained that it was the political taint that had kept him off the air-waves. Ed Sullivan's Show persisted in ignoring him while hiring many lesser talents. Because of the very phantom nature of the blacklist, Josh could never prove that the exclusion from certain shows was because of taint or talent.

However, he did make several appearances on TV. The most notable was a series of shows on the Granada Television Network in Britain, thirteen half-hour performances that were televised from September 21 to December 14, 1961.

On May 9, 1958, Josh was part of Art Ford's "Jazz Party" on WNTA, a widely applauded performance. In January, 1961, he appeared with his daughters, Fern and Beverly, in a program of songs on the Columbia Broadcasting System television show, "Look Up and Live." The show was part of a series called "The Views of Those Present," dealing with social commentary in the arts.

In January, 1963, Josh was a member of a distinguished panel of folk artists who appeared on the CBS "Dinner With the President," a program of the Anti-Defamation League. Josh scored a high point in his "Free and Equal Blues," and when leaving the Washington hotel where the program was televised, he shook hands with his second President, John F. Kennedy, and Vice President Lyndon Johnson of Texas. Later in the year, Josh also appeared on the American Broadcasting Company's "Hootenanny" series.

In June, 1961, Josh was driving from Detroit to Chicago. As usual, he loved the freedom of the open highway, and he pushed his big Lincoln Continental to the speed limit. Suddenly, a sharp pain cut through his arm and chest. But Josh kept driving. His body had known so many pains that this was just another in the medical catalogue. But he was worried. In Chicago, with Negro friends on the South Side where he would find some anonymity from the show world, he rested. He was persuaded to call a doctor, and the pains were diagnosed as a heart attack.

Josh spent six weeks in Michael Reese Hospital, recuperating. Knowing how hard he drove himself, many feared this would be his final illness. Josh asked for his guitar. He asked Memphis Slim (Peter Chatham), the Chicago blues and boogie-woogie man, for the words to an old song, "Going Down Slow":

I done had my fun, if I don't get well no more,
I done had my fun, if I don't get well no more,
My health is failing me
And I know I'm going down slow.

Again, the smell of death was in Josh's nostrils. But the drive, the energy, the will to go on persisted. Chicago disk jockeys played his records with great frequency. Soon, Josh was back in the ring again, singing live, flushed with a new life, although slowed down by the warning his body had given him.

On September 23, 1961, Josh returned again to Manhattan's Town Hall, an auditorium he knew well. Few in the audience knew that Josh had been ill. News of his heart attack had been kept quiet. To the uninitiate, Josh was as youthful and full of fire as ever. His son, Josh Jr., appeared with him, and his daughter, Mrs. Beverly White Saunders, surprised her father by appearing on stage.

Even though the audience could not sense the reason for the sentimental journey the family was making that night, there was an air of celebration at Town Hall that they did sense. It was one of Josh's finest concerts. There were many old favorites, "Outskirts of Town," "Foggy Dew," "Lass With the Delicate Air," and then father, son and daughter joined in "Green Grass Grows All Around."

No, they couldn't put the old fighter out to pasture with just a heart attack. He had many, many long years of performing ahead of him. Whatever happened to his body, the spirit remained youthful. He continued to be close to his five children, and from them learned the meaning of how to remain eternally youthful while growing older.

11 - The House I Live In

The house I live in—the same for black and white.
My country right or wrong—if it's wrong, to set it right;
A land where all are equal,
The house I want to see,
Where all will have four freedoms,
That's America to me.

ONE OF THE qualities that has always distinguished Josh White has been his energy. He has always had time for everything—social action and social play. The public has had only a slight hint of how much time he has had for his family.

Between tours on two continents, across and back the American landscape, Josh did the seemingly impossible—he maintained a close and good relationship with his children and grandchildren. Carol White bore the burden of rearing the five children, but Josh, besides being the provider, was always no further than a phone call away when a decision had to be made about the family.

The house Josh lives in is a sturdy old brick apartment house on West 150th Street, where Harlem and Washington Heights meet in Manhattan's upper West Side. There, in five rooms crowded with furniture, but alive with the smell of cooking and the cleanliness of a good house well kept, lives the family of Josh White.

The children are Blondelle, twenty-seven years old; Mrs. Beverly White Saunders, twenty-three; Joshua Donald (Josh Jr.), twenty-two; Carolyn Fern, nineteen, and Judith (Lovebug), fifteen. To all, music has been a background and foreground of their lives. To all, their often absent father has been an idol and a model.

Closest to Josh has been Donny, who calls himself Josh Jr. on stage. The son became a music student when as only a toddler he blew on a milk bottle as if it were a musical instrument. When he was four, Josh Jr. was taken to Cafe Society and nearly stole the show from his dad.

Hoping that another trouper would emerge from the household, Josh began to teach his son the guitar. At seven, Josh Jr. was touring with his father, standing on piano benches to reach the microphone. The son's self-assurance and stage presence developed so early that he appeared to be "a natural" for a musical career. While still a boy soprano, the parental influence of the sliding blues notes was already in his voice. He appeared in two Broadway plays, *The Man* and *Touchstone*, which won him a best child-star award.

Josh Jr. weathered the change-of-voice era well and emerged with a rich and lustrous baritone. As time passed, he also moved from being a simple carbon copy of his father into a stylist of his own. Solo appearances at Gerde's Folk City and elsewhere were beginning to establish the son as a performer in his own right.

Many feel that the best singer among the children is Beverly, whose jazz stylings have caused widespread praise. Beverly and Josh Jr. attended the Professional Children's High School in Manhattan, and in the early Fifties both sang at commencement exercises at the school and entertained at hospitals around New York with their father.

Beverly was a musical late-comer compared to her brother. But her parents gave her a lot of encouragement, and in 1950 she made her debut on the Arthur Godfrey television show. In 1951 she accompanied her father on his European tour and appeared with him and Josh Jr. on a CBS show in 1961. Beverly and her brother and father tried an extensive series of sessions in Nashville, Tennessee, for Mercury Records, but the sessions just didn't take. She can be heard on the "Josh White at Town Hall" album on Mercury.

Everyone close to Josh thinks that his relationships with children are among the most endearing parts of his personality. Deeply burned in his memory is the fact that "he never had a childhood." He remembers the harshness and deprivations of his youth in Greenville and on the road with the blind men. None of his children or grandchildren would want for material things, but mostly, they would not want for love, acceptance and encouragement.

Sam Freifeld, Josh's lawyer in Chicago, recalls occasions when the singer would relax playing on the floor with Freifeld's children for hours at a time. The warm and loving quality in Josh seems to be one that responds mostly to children and to which children respond quickly. His broad, confiding smile is no stage appurtenance, but the natural warmth of a kind man, a man who finds his greatest joy with youth.

Despite the fact that Josh was the product of the rural singing tradition and the Northern city nightclub, he has been turning increasingly toward the college concert. He likes the ready appreciation of his young listeners and finds with them a close rapport.

A concert in February, 1963, at Vassar College was typical. Josh arrived, in a rented Cadillac, with his manager, Len Rosenfeld; his manager's assistant, Peter Paul; his secretary, and two friends. For the eager audience of one thousand, Josh sang many of his old favorites: the story of the man who got only "One Meat Ball," the gallows defiance of "Samuel Hall," the sweet lyricism of "Scarlet Ribbons."

On the program were songs of social protest. Josh "dedicated" to Governor Ross Barnett of Mississippi the song, "Marching Down Freedom's Road." His irony was inescapable. Josh is no longer in the middle of the fight for Negro rights. After being badly bitten he is doubly cautious about any sort of organizational affiliation. He has been described today as a "one-man Freedom Rider" who will sing to Southern students and socialize with them after concerts, doing in this manner what others are trying to achieve in their sit-ins and demonstrations.

However, Josh played an important role in the famous Freedom March on August 28, 1963, when 210,000 Negroes and whites demonstrated in orderly fashion in Washington, D.C. Josh was seen on television by millions throughout the world as one who sang for the marchers.

The Vassar concert closed with "Strange Fruit," and it still rang with a compelling intensity. After the concert, with a towel around his neck like a prizefighter at the showers, Josh greeted the students who came to his dressing room. For each that asked, Josh gave an autograph but insisted, as is his custom, on a personalized inscription to each. He explained to one girl where he had learned a certain song. He picked up the guitar to explain to another student just what guitar chords he used.

The guitar style of Josh White is without parallel. Some have compared its origins to Blind Lemon Jefferson, Scrapper Blackwell and Lonnie Johnson. Josh has been said to have a "built-in metronome" with his rhythmic beat. He avoids the finger picks used by most country guitarists, but instead, uses his sometimes raw and aching fingers for all the effects.

The particular resonance he achieves on his twenty-seven-year-old Martin 002 guitar are from bronze and Black Diamond all-steel strings. Whether he plays straightforward chords, attenuated single-string figures or "sexy" guitar, the sounds have become as much a Josh White hallmark as has his voice, the foot he places on a chair, the carefully phrased pauses, the songs, always the songs.

As the Cadillac edged its way through the snow away from the Vassar campus, Josh joked with his troupe about the next concerts—concerts that would take him into the Deep South where he had already sung to a quarter-million white students. He had a winter cold and his elbow and shoulder were wracked with the pain of bursitis. Maybe another bout in a hospital lay ahead of him.

But the concert had gone well, and he thought he must sing for more of the kids. They knew what he was saying and he understood them. Pretty soon, he hoped, Josh and Beverly and maybe Fern would be on their way to careers of their own. By the summer, Josh Jr. would be acting in the daytime television series about a lawyer, "Ben Jerrod." Other hopeful signs were in the air for his children and for him.

The snow was melting in the afternoon sun as the large car moved down the highway to New York. For a moment or two everyone in the car was silent. "I think it's going to be a good spring," Josh White said.

Josh White Sings

Blues

Of this plaintive blues song, Josh says: "There are very few happy blues.
This was written in Philadelphia or Chicago, I can't pinpoint it. I first heard
this around 1928 or 1929." As he sings it you can hear the train pulling
out with his woman on it. But there is a note of hope that he'll find
another soon.

Number 12 Train

Music and Words by Josh White

Num-ber Twelve Train _____ took my ba - by _____ I could not keep from cry'n' _____

She left me all night long, I could not help myself
She left me all night long, I could not help myself
I thought she was loving me — I found she had someone else.

I may be wrong but I'll be right some day
I may be wrong but I'll be right some day
'Cause the next gal I get will have to do what papa say.

The singer believes this to be "one of my strongest numbers." He first heard this blues from a Blind Blake (not the singer from the Bahamas), but again made the changes to it that meant greater self-expression. Josh also wrote a woman's version of the song for Libby Holman.

Evil Hearted Me

Well, she even cooked my breakfast
And she brought it to my bed
I took a sip of coffee
Threw the cup at her head.

Chorus: Because I was evil, evil-hearted me . . .

Well, I'm sold out to the devil
Trouble is all I crave
I'd rather see you dead
And laying in your grave.

Chorus: Because I'm evil, evil-hearted me . . .

Now, I don't even care
If it rains from now on
And the gal I love
Had never been born.

Chorus: Because I'm evil, evil-hearted me . . .

Well, I don't even care
If my baby leaves me flat
I got forty 'leven others
If it comes to that.

Chorus: Because I'm evil, evil-hearted me . . .

I'm gonna sing this verse, and I ain't gonna sing no more
(Now ain't you happy? Great God a-mighty)
Sing this verse, ain't gonna sing no more
Kick your husband outa bed, put him right down on the floor.

Words and music by William Weldon. Josh learned it from a disk by
Louis Jordan in 1944. The song's solution to the eternal problem of
infidelity has both its humorous and its savage qualities.

Outskirts of Town

By Andy Razaf and William Weldon

I'm__ gon - na   move_____ 'way out on the out - skirts of

town_____   I'm gon - na   move_____ 'way out on the out - skirts of

town, 'cause I don't want no-bo-dy

who's al - ways hang-in' 'round. _____ Now

(TACET)
let me tell you ba-by, gon-na move you 'way 'way from here, _ Don't want no

ice-man _____ gon-na buy you fri-gid-aire _When we move

ain't gon-na sing it no more. Put your

man in your bed and put your hus-band down on the floor.

Wake up every morning, low-down and dirty shame
Got your men, baby, peckin' on my window pane
That's why I'm gonna move you 'way out on the outskirts of town
'Cause I don't want nobody who's always hangin' 'round.

Well, it may seem funny, honey, funny as it can be
If I have any children, let 'em all look like me
When we move 'way out on the outskirts of town
'Cause I don't want nobody who's always hangin' 'round.

I saw you wigglin' and gigglin', I'm mad as I can be
We've got seven children and none of them looks like me
That's why I'm gonna leave you 'way out on the outskirts of town
'Cause I don't want nobody who's always hangin' 'round.

A traditional blues from the days Josh spent with Joel Walker. Josh likens it in its impact and melodiousness to "St. Louis Blues." He has added new verses to it.

Red River

Music and Words by Josh White

Which a - way, _____ which a - way, _____ does that

The woman I love swears she's goin' back home
Every time I think about her, makes my blood run warm.

Now, the woman I love, she caught that Southbound train
She's a married woman, but I love her just the same.

Did you get that letter that I dropped in your backyard?
I'd come and see you, baby, but your bad man's got me barred.

I walked and I walked till my feet got soaking wet
I was lookin' for my baby, I ain't found her yet.

Sometimes I think I will, and again I think I won't
Sometimes I think I'll kill her, and again I think I won't.

Repeat first verse

Josh converted the traditional "See, See Rider" into a personal blues statement. Also known as "Easy Rider," the original referred to a man who lived off his woman. In its earlier version it was sung by Big Bill Broonzy and Leadbelly. Believed to stem from an unknown Arkansas blues man in the Nineteen Twenties.

Baby, Baby

Music by Josh White / Words by Libby Reynolds Holmes

Ba — by, ba – by, _____ look-a here what you done done,

59

I laid right down, I tried to take my rest
Lord, Lord, Lord
Laid right down, I tried to take my rest
Oh, I laid right down, I tried to take my rest
But my mind kept ramblin'
Like wild geese in the West.

Just as sure as a bird flyin' the skies above
Lord, Lord, Lord
Sure as a bird flyin' the skies above
Just as sure as a bird flyin' the skies above
Life ain't worth livin'
If you ain't with the one you love.

But the sun's gonna shine in my back door some day
Lord, Lord, Lord
Sun's gonna shine in my back door some day
The sun's gonna shine in my back door some day
And the wind's gonna rise, baby
And blow my blues away.

Spirituals

A parable from the Bible, which Josh adapted from his mother's singing. Lazarus, the poor man, and Dives, the rich man, spin out a tale of selfishness and generosity. The famous line, "God gave Noah the rainbow sign, no more water but fire next time," provided the titles for books by Alan Lomax and James Baldwin. The song provides Josh with one of his strongest religious and moral messages.

Home In That Rock

Traditional

home _____ in that ___ rock, don't you see? _____ I've got a

Poor man Laz'rus, poor as I, don't you see
Poor man Laz'rus, poor as I, don't you see
Poor man Laz'rus, poor as I, when he died he had a home on high
Had a home in that rock, don't you see.

Rich man Dives he lived so well, don't you see
Rich man Dives lived so well, don't you see
Rich man Dives lived so well, when he died he made a home in Hell
Had no home in that rock, don't you see.

Written by Carol and Josh White around 1939. It was in the ebbing years of the Depression, and both were down in the dumps spiritually and searching for hope and for answers. This modern spiritual, originally recorded by Josh on Columbia, reflects their search in song.

Lord Have Mercy

Traditional / New Music and Words by Josh White

1. Lord, Lord, have mer-cy
2. You delivered Dan-iel

Have mer - cy when I come to die Lord, Lord, have mer-
You from the li - on's den Yes, you de - liv-ered

- cy, mer - cy when I come to die.
Daniel, do, Lord, re - mem - ber me.

My mother's gone and left me
Down in this world alone
I've got no friends or relations
Trying to make heaven my home.

Chorus: Lord, Lord have mercy . . .

A personification of death, taking loved ones away. Josh White learned this old spiritual as a child, subsequently changed the words and the melody to meet his own needs, as is typical of the folk process. He inserted this historical line: "He took Abe Lincoln's name, There were no slaves left in chains."

Takin' Names

Traditional

He took that liar's name, takin' names
Well, he took that liar's name, takin' names
Oh, he took that liar's name, his tongue got twisted and he died in shame
There's a man goin' 'round takin' names.

Never let him catch you with your work undone when he takes your name
Never let him catch you with your work undone when he takes your name
Never let him catch you with your work undone, if you do hell will be
    your home
There's a man goin' 'round takin' names.

He took Abe Lincoln's name, takin' names
Yes, he took Abe Lincoln's name, takin' names
He took Abe Lincoln's name but there were no slaves left in chains
There's a man goin' 'round takin' names.

Repeat first verse

A Biblical theme infuses this spiritual of the two prophets. Josh was "teethed" on this song from his mother. Also known as "All Night Long," it has a long history in the call and response of the Negro folk church. Its reference to bondage in jail has given the song new relevance as a "Freedom Song" in the South today.

Who Shall Deliver Poor Me

(OR PAUL AND SILAS)

Traditional

Ja - cob rass-led with the an - gels ____ all ___ night long ____

Paul and Silas bound in jail all night long *(3 times)*
Who shall deliver poor me?

Paul prayed and Silas moaned all night long *(3 times)*
Who shall deliver poor me?

Paul and Silas bound in jail all night long *(3 times)*
Who shall deliver poor me?

Believe in the Lord and you shall be saved all night long *(3 times)*
Who shall deliver poor me?

A bright-tempoed religious song of recent composition. The reference to the fish is Biblical, from the time when the Canaanites paid their taxes with fish.

Run, Mona, Run

Traditional / New Music and Words by Josh White

God Al-might-y cre-a-ted this world___ He made___ the sun,___ He made___ the moon,___ He made the stars, just to give us a light.___ Now___

to CHORUS

Note: The verses may be lengthened or shortened in a free, recitative, "preacher" style.

'Twas I, the Lord who had pity upon
Converted my soul
He gave me a stone
And none can read it
But he who received it
And I received it
And I can read it
And just let me tell you what the stone did say
Says, Redeemer, Redeemer
I been born to God
Washed in the Blood of the Lamb.

Chorus: Run, Mona, run, heaven is a-shouting . . .

Simon, Simon
He'd a-go to the brook
He casted your hook
Pull up the fish
And open his mouth
Take out the money
And go and pay taxes for a-you and me.

Chorus: Run, Mona, run, heaven is a-shouting . . .

Believed to be another spiritual that freely mixes references to the New and Old Testaments, all in a brisk tempo and light mood. This is related to several Jonah and the Whale songs, one of which was first published in *Old Plantation Hymns* in 1899. These are believed, however, to have been used more as college glee-club songs than as spirituals.

Peter (OR JONAH)

Traditional

Who did, who did, who did, who did
Who did swallow Jonah, Jonah? } *(3 times)*
Who did swallow Jonah? *(2 times)*
Who did swallow Jonah whole?

The whale did, the whale did the whale did,
  the whale did } *(3 times)*
The whale did swallow Jonah, Jonah.
The whale did swallow Jonah *(2 times)*
The whale did swallow Jonah whole.

Jonah, Jonah, Jonah, Jonah
Jonah in the whale's belly. } *(3 times)*
Jonah in the belly *(2 times)*
Jonah in the belly whole.

Daniel, Daniel, Daniel, Daniel
Daniel in the lion. } *(3 times)*
Daniel in the lion *(2 times)*
Daniel in the lion's den.

Repeat first verse

A particularly affecting old spiritual, first recorded by Josh White on August 15, 1933, under the name of the Singing Christian. He had learned it at the Church of God in the Saints of Christ in Greenville. The personalized affinity with Jesus, a kinship born of suffering, is reflected. The phrase about meeting in the middle of the air "if these wings should fail me" is to be found in many old spirituals.

Jesus Gonna Make Up My Dyin' Bed

Traditional

All I want my friends to do, come and fold my dy-in' arms

CHORUS

Well, well, well, so I can die ea-sy Well, well, well,

Well, well, well, so

I can die ea-sy, Je-sus gon-na make up my dy-in' bed.

(Jesus Gonna Make Up My Dyin' Bed *continued*)

Every since I been acquainted with my Jesus
We haven't been a minute apart
He placed the receiver in my hand
And put religion in my heart.

Chorus:
Well, well, well, I can ring up my Jesus
Well, well, well, I can talk to my Jesus
Well, well, well, I can call up Jesus
Jesus gonna make up my dyin' bed.

My Lord don't mind me calling
I'm blind, crippled and lame
My train is waiting at the station
I hear the Captain calling my name.

Chorus:
Well, well, well, I hear my Captain calling *(3 times)*
Jesus gonna make up my dyin' bed.

When I'm dead and buried
Somebody's going to say I'm lost
Follow me down to the river
And ask the ferry man didn't I cross.

Chorus:
Well, well, well, I've done crossed over *(3 times)*
Jesus gonna make up my dyin' bed.

Goin' on down to the river
Stick my sword up in the sand
I'm gonna shout my troubles over
I've made it to the Promised Land.

Chorus:
Well, well, well, I've done crossed over *(3 times)*
Jesus gonna make up my dyin' bed.

Meet me, Jesus, meet me
Meet me in the middle of the air
And if these wings should fail me
Lord, meet me with another pair.

Chorus:
Well, well, well, won't you meet me Jesus *(3 times)*
Jesus gonna make up my dyin' bed.
Meet me, Jesus, meet me
Meet me in the middle of the air
You promised me ten thousand years ago
You'd be standin' there.

Chorus:
Well, well, well, won't you meet me Jesus *(3 times)*
Jesus gonna make up my dyin' bed.

A very old Negro spiritual. Josh's first recollection of the song is as a child
in Greenville, singing with his brothers and sisters.

So Soon in the Mornin'

Traditional

soon in the morn-in', a-when the clouds roll a-way, So

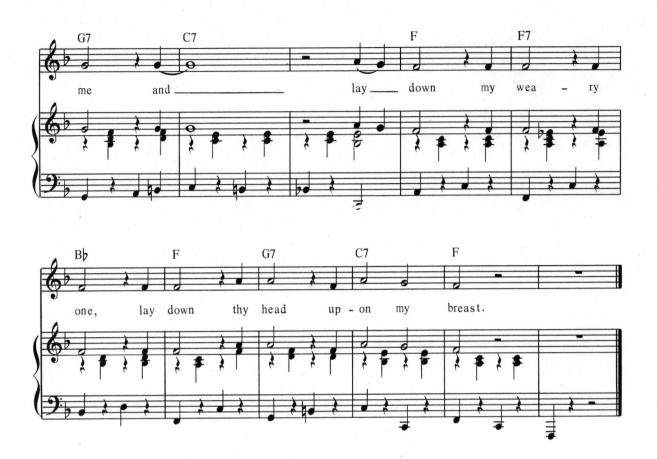

me and _____ lay ___ down my wea – ry

one, lay down thy head up – on my breast.

Oh, Lord, I stretch my hand to Thee
No other help I know
If Thou withdraw Thy hand from me
Oh, where shall I go?

Chorus: So soon in the mornin', a-when the clouds roll away . . .

I'm standin' at the station with my ticket in my hand
I'm standin' at the station tryin' to make the Promised Land
I'll hope and I'll trust and I'll watch through the night
So soon in the mornin' when the dark clouds roll away.

Chorus: So soon in the mornin', a-when the clouds roll away . . .

79

A timeless retelling of the Crucifixion story, long in Negro tradition. Josh learned it at home.

He Never Said a Mumblin' Word

Traditional

They cru - ci - fied my Lord. And He ne - ver said a mum - bl - in' word. And they

They hung Him on the cross
And He never said a mumblin' word
They hung Him on the cross
And He never said a mumblin' word
Not a word, not a word, not a word.

They pierced Him in the side
And He never said a mumblin' word
They pierced Him in the side
And He never said a mumblin' word
Not a word, not a word, not a word.

And the blood came trickling down
And He never said a mumblin' word
The blood came trickling down
And He never said a mumblin' word
Not a word, not a word, not a word.

He just hung His head and died
But He never said a mumblin' word
He just hung His head and died
But He never said a mumblin' word
Not a word, not a word, not a word.

Some have attributed this joyous song to Mahalia Jackson. "It says what I believe in, what I am," declares Josh. "I try to live what I sing about."

Gonna Live the Life I Sing About

Music and Words by Thomas A. Dorsey

I'm gon - na live,___ live___ the life I sing a - bout___ down in my soul, oh yes,___ in my

(2nd time) Hum _ _ _ _ _ _ _ _ _ _ _ _ _ _ _ _ _ _ _

soul _____ I'm gon-na fight _____ for _____ the right _____ And shun the
(Hum) - - - *(sing)*

wrong, _____ shun _____ the wrong. _____ Out in the street, _____ or in my

home, _____ if I have com - pa - ny or I'm a - lone, _____ I'm gon-na

rit. 2nd time

live _____ live _____ the life I sing a - bout _____ down in my soul, oh yes, _____ in my soul. _____

Ev – 'ry day, _____ ev – 'ry – where, _____ on this

bu – sy _____ tho – rough – fare, _____ peo – ple

shun me, _____ look down up – on me, _____ they _____ don't

like me _____ I _____ don't care _____ I can't sing_

I'm gonna live the life I sing about in my song
I'm gonna step right and always shun the wrong
If I'm in a crowd
If I'm alone
On the street
Or in my home
I'm gonna live the life I sing about in my song.

If by day, if at night
I must always walk by the light
So mistake me, underrate me
Because I want to do right
I can't go to church and shout all day Sunday
Go out and get drunk and raise sand on Monday
I've got to live the life I sing about in my song.

Another of the Old Testament-inspired spirituals in which the American
Negro found an easy parallel to his own oppression, whether in slavery
or in the life that followed slavery. Josh learned this hopeful spiritual about
a future of freedom when he was a boy.

I Don't Intend To Die in Egypt Land

I don't in-tend to stop, I
don't in-tend to stand, I don't in-tend to die in E - gypt land. ___ I
don't in - tend to stop till ___ I reach the Prom - ised Land, I

The tallest tree in Paradise
I don't intend to die in Egypt land
The people down there call it "The Tree of Life"
I don't intend to die in Egypt land.

Chorus: Lord, I can't stay away, Lord, I can't stay away . . .

The Pilate's wife, she had a dream
I don't intend to die in Egypt land
That an honest man she seen
I don't intend to die in Egypt land.

Chorus: Lord, I can't stay away, Lord, I can't stay away . . .

She said, "Go bring me some water, let me wash my hands"
I don't intend to die in Egypt land
"I shan't be guilty of an innocent man"
I don't intend to die in Egypt land.

Chorus: Lord, I can't stay away, Lord, I can't stay away . . .

Repeat first verse

Chorus: Lord, I can't stay away, Lord, I can't stay away . . .

A song widely associated with Ethel Waters, and the title of her autobiography. Josh recalls singing the old spiritual long before he met Ethel in New York.

His Eye Is On The Sparrow

spar - row, And I know He wat - ches o - ver me. And I

CHORUS

a tempo - slow bounce

sing ____ be - cause ____ I'm hap - py, ____

____ Oh yes, I just sing ____ be - cause ____ I'm

free. ____ His eye ____ is

Sometimes my way gets cloudy
And sometimes my work seems in vain
Sometimes my soul feels lonely
The world has me bound down in chains
'Tis then I call on Jesus
He hears me though I, I can't explain
Then down comes the holy spirit
And my soul feels good again
Then down comes the holy spirit
And my soul feels good again.

Chorus: And I sing because I'm happy . . .

A parable from the Bible. Josh finds the story an endearing one, which means to him, "If we all work together, the whole world could be fed." A testament to belief and to brotherhood.

Two Little Fishes (AND FIVE LOAVES OF BREAD)

Music and Words by Bernie Hanighen

A crowd of peo-ple went out on the de-sert,_____ to lis-ten to the Good Lord's word._____ All day long_____ they heard_____ the Good_

Lord's word ___ They got hun - gry ___ and had to be fed ___ On on - ly

CHORUS

two ___ lit - tle fish - es, and ___ five loaves of bread, Two lit - tle

fish - es, and five ___ loaves of bread. ___

Final Ending

Cm ... Ab7 ... Cm ... *Fine*

loaves of bread ___ Two lit - tle fish - es, and five ___ loaves of bread. ___

Slow - free

G7

Hear what I've said, If we all work to - ge - ther, then the

A 7 ... G7 ... *a tempo*

world could be fed, On on - ly

to CHORUS

The Lord's disciples began to get worried
And each of them scratched their heads
What could they do, each one knew
There was a big crowd that had to be fed.

Chorus: On only two little fishes and five loaves of bread . . .

The Lord said to his disciples, "Don't you get worried
Bring me the loaves of bread instead
Bring the fishes by, let me try a little idea
I got in my head."

Chorus: About those two little fishes and five loaves of bread . . .

They brought the bread and the fishes
And the disciples went on ahead
The more they passed 'round, the more they found with lots left over
When all had been fed.

Chorus: On only two little fishes and five loaves of bread . . .

An old spiritual based on the parable from the Book of Luke about the beggar Lazarus and the rich man Dives.

Dip Your Fingers in the Water

Traditional

CHORUS

Old Fa-ther Ab - ra - ham,___ pray let La - z'us come, And dip his fin - gers in the wa - ter, come and cool my tongue, 'cause

Extended ending of VERSE 4 (and also final CHORUS)

And he begged the crumbs that fell from the rich man's table.

Chorus:
A-dip his fingers in the water
Come and cool my tongue
'Cause I'm tormented in the flame.

They sic'd the dogs to drive that poor man away.

Chorus: A-dip his fingers in the water . . .

But the dogs had compassion and licked that poor man's sores.

Chorus: A-dip his fingers in the water . . .

Leader, with group response:
Got five brothers
I'm tormented
Yonder's world
I'm tormented
Please go tell them
I'm tormented
Don't come here
I'm tormented
Don't come here
I'm tormented.

Chorus: Lord, a-dip his fingers in the water . . .

Leader, with group response:
Dip your fingers
I'm tormented
Lord, won't hear me
I'm tormented
My soul's on fire
I'm tormented
One drop of water
I'm tormented
To cool my tongue, Lord
I'm tormented
Cool my tongue, Lord
I'm tormented.

(2 times)

Chorus: Lord, a-dip his fingers in the water . . .

Another widely known spiritual of affirmation. Josh thinks it was "brought to life by Mahalia [Jackson]."

Whole World in His Hands

Traditional

He's got you and me, brother, in his hand
He's got you and me, brother, in his hand
He's got you and me, brother, in his hand
He's got the whole world in his hand.

Chorus: He's got the whole world in his hand . . .

He's got the little bitty babies in his hand *(3 times)*
He's got the whole world in his hand.

Chorus: He's got the whole world in his hand . . .

He's got the lyin' man in his hand *(3 times)*
He's got the whole world in his hand.

Chorus: He's got the whole world in his hand . . .

He's got the gamblin' man in his hand *(3 times)*
He's got the whole world in his hand.

Chorus: He's got the whole world in his hand . . .

Ad lib verses

98

Songs of Protest

Learned from one of the blind singers. This old classic fuses two of the most prevalent themes in Negro folk song, the train and the prison. Believed to come from the Texas State Prison Farm at Sugarland. The Golden Gate Limited leaves Houston at midnight, and prison legend has it that if the light from the train hits your jail window you will be freed the next day.

Midnight Special

Traditional

Hey,   look-a, look-a

yon - der,_____ what in the world do I see?_____

___That mid-night___ spe-cial_____ with it's___ light_on__ me._____

If you ever go to Houston, well you better walk right
You better not stagger and you better not fight
The sheriff will arrest you and he'll take you down
You bet your bottom dollar that you're jailhouse bound.

Chorus: Let the Midnight Special shine its light on me . . .

Well, you wake up in the mornin', hear the ding dong ring
Go a-marchin' to the table, see the same damn thing
On the table is a knife, fork and a pan
Say anything about it, you're in trouble with the man.

Chorus: Let the Midnight Special shine its light on me . . .

Yonder come Doctor Melton, how in the world do I know
He gave me a tablet three or four days ago
There never was a doctor, travelled by land
That could cool the fever of a convict man.

Chorus: Let the Midnight Special shine its light on me . . .

Hey look-a look-a yonder, what in the world do I see
I see my baby comin' after me
She brought me a little coffee, she brought me a little tea
She brought me everything but the jailhouse key.

Chorus: Let the Midnight Special shine its light on me . . .

101

Waring Cuney gets the credit for this song, first recorded on "Southern Exposure." Josh converted Cuney's lyrics somewhat, removing the dialect which he dislikes. It is a hard-hitting song of protest, not just about the Negro oppressed, but about the white oppressed, too. It reflects the whole era of the sharecropper's misery in the South.

Hard Time Blues (OR HARD TIMES)

Traditional / New Music and Words by Josh White

Well, I went down home 'bout a year a-go Things so bad,—Lord,— my heart—was sore— Folks had noth-in', it was a

Now the sun was a-shinin' fourteen days and no rain
Hoeing and planting was all in vain
They had hard, hard times, Lord, all around
Meal barrels empty, crops burnt to the ground.

Chorus: Great God a-mighty, folks feelin' bad . . .

They had skinny lookin' children, bellies poking out
That old Pellagry without a doubt
Old folk hangin' 'round the cabin door
Ain't seen times so hard before.

Chorus: Great God a-mighty, folks feelin' bad . . .

Well, I went to the boss at the commissary store
Folks all starvin', please don't close your door
We want more food and a little more time to pay
Boss man laughed and walked away.

Chorus: Great God a-mighty, folks feelin' bad . . .

Now your landlord comes around when your rent it is due
And if you ain't got his money he'll take your home from you
He'll take your mule and horse, even take your cow
Get off my land, you're no good no how.

Chorus: Great God a-mighty, folks feelin' bad . . .

Josh says this is the first song of his own composition that he recorded.
It was issued under the name of Pinewood Tom on the American-Perfect
label in 1936. One of the most direct protest statements in the blues,
detailing the destruction of prisoners' health by work in the earth.

Silicosis Blues

Traditional / New Music and Words by Josh White

Si - li - co - sis, you made a

might-y bad break of me

Si - li - co - sis, you made a might-y bad break of me

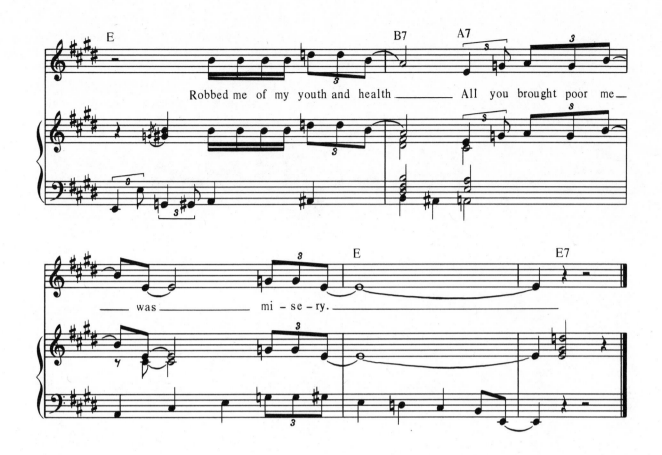

Silicosis, you're a dirty robber and a thief
Yes, silicosis, you're a dirty robber and a thief
Robbed me of my right to live and all you brought poor me was grief.

I was there diggin' that tunnel for just six bits a day
I was diggin' that tunnel for just six bits a day
Didn't know I was diggin' my grave—silicosis was eatin' my lungs away.

Six bits I got for diggin'—mmm, diggin' that tunnel hole
I got for diggin'—six bits for diggin' that tunnel hole
Takes me 'way from my baby and sure done wrecked my soul.

I says, Mama, Mama, Mama, please cool my fevered head
I says, Mama, Mama, Mama, cool my fevered head
Going to meet my Jesus, God knows I'll soon be dead.

Now, tell all my buddies, tell my friends you see
Tell all my buddies, tell my friends you see
I'm going 'way up yonder and please don't grieve for me.

An original by Josh White, written for the 1940 "Chain Gang" album on Columbia. A protest song in words of strength that never equivocate.

Goin' Home Boys

Music and Words by Josh White

Goin'_____ home, boys, _____ Cry'n won't make_____ me stay_____ My

time is up_____ throw these chains___ a-way_____ Now,

when they brought me here, boys, I lost my broth - er, too.

White folks took and shot him, was noth-in' I could do. But I'm goin'_____

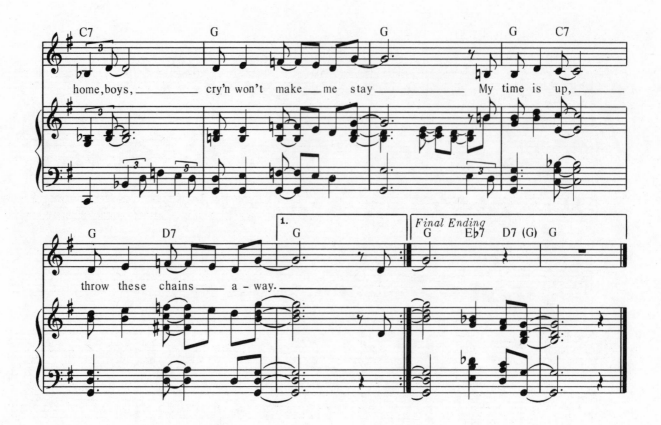

home, boys, _____ cry'n won't make _____ me stay _____ My time is up, _____ throw these chains _____ a - way.

Now when they brought me here, boys, I lost my brother, too
White folks took and shot him, was nothin' I could do
But I'm goin' home, boys, cryin' won't make me stay
My time is up, throw these chains away.

I heard from my mama, her letter made me cry
If she could only see me, I'm sure she'd surely die
But I'm goin' home, boys, cryin' won't make me stay
My time is up, throw these chains away.

Just as sure as the train, boys, rolls up in the yard
I'm gonna leave this rock pile if I have to ride the rods
My time is up, throw these chains away.

Josh wrote the words to this song, to the melody of "Going Down the
Road Feeling Bad." Originally recorded on Keynote in 1940. You can
hear the train wheels, whistle bell and the trestle in the accompaniment.
You can hear the call of justice in the lyrics.

Jim Crow Train

Traditional / New Words by Josh White

Stop the train so I can ride
Stop Jim Crow so I can ride
Stop Jim Crow so I can ride
Black and white folk ridin' side by side.

Can't you hear that train whistle blow?
Can't you hear that train whistle blow?
Can't you hear that train whistle blow?
Oh, Lord, that train is Jim Crow.
Goddam Jim Crow.

Repeat first verse

109

Lewis Allan wrote this most powerful of the protest songs rooted in racial oppression. Josh says it is requested almost as frequently in the South as in the North. In performances overseas, Josh always follows it with "The House I Live In," to counter the unfavorable impression of America created by "Strange Fruit."

Strange Fruit

Music and Words by Lewis Allan

rain to gath-er, ___ for the wind to ___ suck For the sun to rot, for the trees to dro - - - p Oh, ___ here is a strange and bitter ___ crop.

Oh, ___ here is a strange ___ and bi - tter crop. ___

112

Ballads

A song about a railroad man's daughter. Originally entitled "Black Gal."
This song was the cause of a dispute at the London Records plant here
in 1952. Some Negroes working there misunderstood the intent of the
lyrics and felt it was derogatory toward their race, and they refused to
process the recording. Josh states: "There is nothing derogatory about it."
He recalls that Leadbelly had been hooted off stage when he tried to sing
the song at the Golden Gate Ballroom for a Negro audience.

Black Girl

Traditional

where _____ did you stay _____ last night? _____ In the pines, _____ in the pines, _____ where the sun _____ nev-er shines _____ And I shiv-er'd _____ the whole _____ night through. _____

My husband was a railroad man
Killed a mile and a half from here
His head was found 'neath the driver's wheel, and
His body has never been found.

Guitar interlude:
It cause me to weep, cause me to moan
And it cause me to leave my home.

Black girl, black girl, where will you go?
I'm going where the cold wind blows
In the pines, in the pines, where the sun never shines
And I'll shiver the whole night through.

A celebrated blues song of the Nineteen Twenties. Recorded by Bessie Smith in May, 1929, and often called her most famous number. Josh, too, found an enormous amount of personal identification in this song, attributed to Jimmie Cox. Says he: "Bessie spent a lot of money on fair-weather friends. And I can count *my* friends on one hand, without the thumb."

Nobody Knows You When You're Down and Out

Music and Words by Jimmie Cox

Once I lived the life___ of a mil - lion-aire___ Spend-ing my mo - ney___ and I did - n't care___ Tak-ing my friends out___ for a

might-y good time___ Buy – ing boot – leg liq – uor, ___ cham-pagne, and wine ___

When I be – gan ___ to fall so low I did-n't have a friend and

no place to go ___ If I ev – er get my hands ___ on a

dol – lar a – gain, I'll hold on to it ___ 'till the ea – gle grins. ___

No _____ no-bo-dy wants you _____

When you're down_____ and out_____ In your pock-et

not one pen - ny And your friends,—you have-n't an - y_____ But as

soon as you get up-on _____ your_____ feet a - gain _____ Ev -'ry

bo-dy wants to be_____ your long lost friend____ It's might-y strange, _____ with-

out a doubt _____ No-bo-dy wants you,_when you're down_and out._

down__and__out. I__mean__when _____ when you're_

____down__and out.____

This story of a murder of passion comes from the Bahamas. Josh calls it a "calypso 'Frankie and Johnny.'" The singer generally lightens the tone of tragedy in the song until he gets to the passage where he talks to the jailer. He first started singing "Delia" in 1939 and recorded it on his twenty-fifth anniversary album (Elektra 123).

Delia (OR DELIA'S GONE)

New Music and Words by Josh White

Delia cursed poor Too-ly,_____ cursed him such a wick-ed curse_____

If he had-n't shot her,_____ she'd a - cursed him ten times

They sent for the doctor
He came all dressed in white
Done everything a doctor could do
But he couldn't save Delia's life.

Chorus: Delia's gone, one more round, Delia's gone . . .

Then her mother, she came a-runnin'
All dressed in black
She cried all day and she cried all night
But she couldn't bring Delia back.

Chorus: Delia's gone, one more round, Delia's gone . . .

On a Monday he was arrested
Tuesday he was tried
Jury-box foun'd him guilty
And the verdict was to die.

Chorus: Delia's gone, one more round, Delia's gone . . .

He said, "Jailer, oh Jailer,
How can I sleep?
All around my bed at night
I can hear little Delia's feet."

One of the most popular songs in Josh's repertoire is this jaunty Australian tune about a jolly wanderer. Josh thinks it is a much sadder song than most people realize. He first sang it during an engagement at the Somerset Hotel in Boston in 1945. The song was written in 1936 by two Australians: words by A. B. Paterson, music by Marie Cowan, Australian troops spread the song around the world during World War II.

Waltzing Matilda

You'll come a-waltz-ing,_____ Ma-til-da,_____ with me._____

Down came a jumbuck to drink beside the billabong
Up jumped the swagman and siezed him with glee
And he sang as he stowed that jumbuck in his tucker bag
"You'll come a-waltzing, Matilda, with me."

Chorus:
Waltzing Matilda, waltzing Matilda
You'll come a-waltzing, Matilda, with me
And he sang as he talked to that jumbuck in his tucker bag
"You'll come a-waltzing, Matilda, with me."

Down came the squatter, riding on his thoroughbred
Down came the troopers, one, two, three
"Where's that jolly jumbuck you've got in your tucker bag?
You'll come a-waltzing, Matilda, with me."

Chorus:
Waltzing Matilda, waltzing Matilda
You'll come a-waltzing, Matilda, with me
"Where's that jolly jumbuck you've got in your tucker bag?
You'll come a-waltzing, Matilda, with me."

Up jumped the swagman and plunged into the billabong
"You'll never catch me alive," cried he
And his ghost may be heard as you ride beside the billabong
"You'll come a-waltzing, Matilda, with me."

Chorus:
Waltzing Matilda, waltzing Matilda
"You'll come a-waltzing, Matilda, with me"
And his ghost may be heard as you ride beside the billabong
"You'll come a-waltzing, Matilda, with me."

Josh characterizes this simply as a story about "a guy in love." The line "She turned my love into hate" is as old as love, as new as the Freudian concept of ambivalence.

When I Lay Down and Die

Now it wasn't for gold she turned me down
But I wouldn't live in her city-town

Now the other fellow might be, but he didn't rob
'Cause livin' with some women is the devil's job.

Yes, she turned my love to hate instead
And I'll still be a-hatin' when I'm dead

When I lay down and die, do die
Bury me where she passes by.

Repeat first two verses

125

A woman's song, one of the most eloquent plaints against the life of prostitution. "I've got to believe what I'm trying to tell," says Josh White, "and I believe this song." He learned "Rising Sun" from a white hillbilly singer in either Winston-Salem or High Point, North Carolina. A few years ago he had to "convince" a folklorist that he hadn't learned it from one of his books or recordings.

House of the Rising Sun

By Nicholas Ray, Josh White and Libby Reynolds Holmes

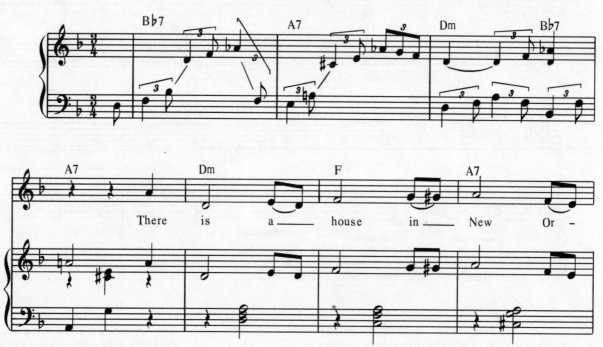

There is a —— house in —— New Or -

Now, if I had a-listened to what my mama said
I'd a-been at home today
But being so young and foolish, oh Lord
I let a rambler lead me astray.

Go tell my baby sister
Don't do what I have done
Please shun that house in New Orleans
They call the Rising Sun.

Lord, I'm going back to New Orleans
My race is almost run
Yes I'm going back to spend my life
Beneath that Rising Sun.

Written by Lewis Allan in the Nineteen Forties, when World War II
forced Americans to take a sobering look at the nature of their democracy.
One of the principal themes of the life of Josh White, this stirring song is
also known as "What is America to Me." Josh says, "I will sing it
anywhere. It is not so much about what we have in America now, but
what we are fighting for. This is the answer to 'Strange Fruit.'"

The House I Live In

Capo on 2nd fret
Actual KEY Bmajor

Music by Charlie D. Tillman / New Words by Josh White

Josh says this has been a white spiritual. He learned it in 1945 when
performing in Colorado. Curiously, there is a song to this general effect
discussed in *Slave Songs of the United States* and *Afro-American
Folksongs*. The linkage is something for the folklorists to theorize upon.

I Know Moonlight

Music and Words by Josh White

I walk in the moonlight, and I walk in the starlight
When I lay this body down.

I go to the judgment in the evening of the day
When I lay this body down.

Mmm . . .
When I lay this body down.

Repeat first verse

132

A song about Franklin Delano Roosevelt.
This tribute had lyrics that Josh showed to Mrs. Roosevelt.
She made some changes in it, Josh changed the music. He first sang it in
Town Hall. About four months after the President's death, in April, 1945,
he sang the song for Mrs. Roosevelt. "It was the only time I ever saw her
cry," he recalls. His earnings from the original recording went to the
March of Dimes.

The Man Who Couldn't Walk Around

Music by Harry Rosenthal / Words by MacKinlay Kantor

Little boy, look up and smile
And grasp the chance he gave you
Let his courage save you
Little boy, though your world is full of sorrow
There is still tomorrow
Even though one sits as still as you.

I'm dreaming of a laugh we heard
The broadest smile, the bravest words
I mean a man who couldn't walk around
He shook the earth, the sky, the seas
And couldn't even move his knees
That certain man who couldn't walk around.

One afternoon in Georgia, he slept away, they say
But people across the ocean still praise his name today.
He's watching from the highest hill
His nerve is in this nation still
That certain man who couldn't walk around.

A spirited breakdown or square-dance tune. Josh, who wrote part of the last two verses, considers it like a lullaby for children. He once used it to lull the youngsters at the Blue Angel.

Cotton-Eyed Joe

Traditional

Where do you come from, and where do you go,

Where do you come from my cot - ton eyed Joe.

Well, I come for to see you, and I come for to sing
I come for to show you my diamond ring.

If it hadn't have been for Cotton-Eyed Joe
Well, I'd have been married a long time ago.

One of the oldest of the "classic" ballads, listed as Child No. 12, and found in such disparate places as Italy of the seventeenth century and the Southern Appalachians of our time. Josh is not sure where he first heard the song, "perhaps from Aunt Molly Jackson." Although there are changes, the essential dialogue between mother and poisoned son remains intact.

Lord Randall

138

Mo - ther _____ I've been to my sweet-heart, Mo - ther, Oh _____ make my bed soon, for I'm sick to my heart and I fain would lie down.

What did she feed you, Randall, my son?
What did she feed you, my handsome one?
A cup of cold poison, Mother
A cup of cold poison, Mother.

Chorus: Oh, make my bed soon . . .

What will you leave your mother, Randall, my son?
What will you leave your mother, my handsome one?
A dead son to bury, Mother
A dead son to bury, Mother.

Chorus: Oh, make my bed soon . . .

What will you leave your sweetheart, Randall, my son?
What will you leave your sweetheart, my handsome one?
A rope to hang her, Mother
A rope from hell to hang her.

Chorus: Oh, make my bed soon . . .

A song of Southern Negro origin. John Jacob Niles tells of first hearing it in 1908 from a ditch-digger. He made some structural and lyrical changes to this lovely, bittersweet love song.

Go Way From My Window

Traditional / New Music and Words by John Jacob Niles

I'll tell all my brothers
And I'll tell my sister, too
The reason why my heart is broken
Is all because of you
It's all because of you.

I'll give you back your letters
And I'll give you back your ring
But I'll remember you my love
As long as songbirds sing
As long as songbirds sing.

Go on your way, be happy
And go on your way and rest
But remember, darling, you're the one
I really did love best
I really did love best.

Repeat first verse

141

Another of the bedrock songs in American balladry, known in scores of versions here and in Britain. Josh first heard it from Richard Dyer-Bennet and "got carried away with it." This sad story of love that failed and death that followed is probably the most widely known ballad in the English language.

Barb'ry Allen

Traditional

In Scar-let Town, where I was born, There was a fair maid dwel-lin',__ Made ev-'ry youth cry, "Lack-a-day".

For her name___ was Bar - b'ry Al - len.___

'Twas in the merry month of May
When green buds they were swellin'
Young William on his death bed lay
For the love of Barb'ry Allen.

He sent his man to the town
To the place where she was dwellin'
You must come to my master dear
If your name be Barb'ry Allen.

Slowly, slowly she got up
And slowly she came nigh him
And all he said, "My dear friends all
Be kind to Barb'ry Allen."

As she was walking o'er the hills
She heard the death bell knellin'
And every stroke it seemed to say
"Hard hearted Barb'ry Allen."

Farewell, farewell my dear friends all
Please shun the fate I fell in
Henceforth take warning of the fault
Of cruel Barb'ry Allen.

Some persons have termed this seventeenth-century English ballad sacrilegious, but Josh regard it differently. "It's really the most natural thing for a man in this position to say"—referring to the expression, "Goddam your eyes!" This song dramatizes the gallows defiance of an earthy character.

Sam Hall

Traditional

Oh, my name it is Sam Hall; it is Sam Hall Now my name it's Sam Hall, it is Sam Hall Yes, my name it's Sam-uel Hall, and I

144

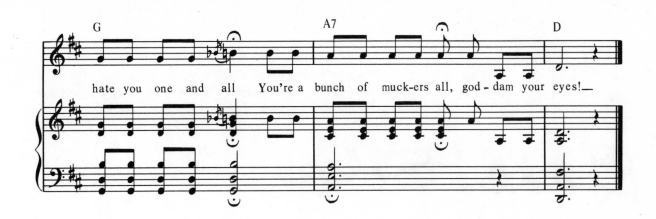

hate you one and all You're a bunch of muck-ers all, god-dam your eyes!

Oh, I killed a man 'tis said, so 'tis said
I killed a man 'tis said, so 'tis said
I killed a man 'tis said, hell — I split his bloody head
And I left him there for dead, goddam his eyes!

Oh, the sheriff he come to, he come to
Now the sheriff he come to, he come to
Oh, the sheriff he come to, with his little boys in blue
Oh Lord, what a bloody crew, goddam their eyes!

And I saw Molly in the crowd, in the crowd
I saw Molly in the crowd, in the crowd
I saw Molly in the crowd, and I hollered right out loud
"Hey, Molly, ain't you proud?" Goddam your eyes!

Oh, the parson he did come, he did come
Now the parson he did come, he did come
Oh, the parson he did come, and he looked so goddam glum
As he talked of Kingdom Come (and he can kiss my
        ruddy bum), god-dam his eyes!

Let this be my parting knell, parting knell
Let this be my parting knell, parting knell
Let this be my parting knell, I'll see you all in hell
And I hope you sizzle well, goddam your eyes!

One of the oldest ballads known in folk music—from England some
eight hundred years ago. Josh says it was a riddle before it was a song.

Riddle Song

Traditional

I gave my love a cher-ry that had no stone

Gave my love a chi-cken that had no bone I told my love a sto-ry

that had no end   I   gave my love a ba-by _____   with no cry-in'. _____

How can there be a cherry that has no stone?
How can there be a chicken that has no bone?
Whoever heard a story that had no end?
How can there be a baby with no cryin'?

Now, a cherry when it's bloomin', it has no stone
A chicken when it's pippin', it has no bone
The story of "I love you" will never end
A baby when it's sleepin', there's no cryin'.

Wanderin'

"Some people say this should be my theme song," says Josh White.

Traditional

My Dad longs to see me home
My brother'd share his bed
My sister yearns for me to have
A roof above my head.

Chorus: And it looks like I'm never gonna cease my wanderin'.

I've wandered early and late
From Singapore to the Golden Gate
I've worked on freighters, I've worked on the farms
And all I've got to show for it is the muscles in my arm.

Chorus: And it looks like I'm never gonna cease my wanderin'.

Snakes in the ocean
And eels in the sea
I let a red-headed woman
Make a fool out of me.

Chorus: And it looks like I'm never gonna cease my wanderin'.

Hum one verse

Chorus: And it looks like I'm never gonna cease my wanderin'.

148

Work Songs

Sam Gary and Josh White wrote this version of "Timber" at the time of the
first "Chain-Gang Album," in the early Nineteen Forties. The melody and
concept are traditional, an embodiment of the oppressed worker in the
form of a mule. Also known as "Jerry," the mule here is in the great
tradition of the indomitable animal—the cutty wren, the darby ram, the
gray goose and Paul Bunyan's ox.

Timber

Music and Words by Josh White

Got-ta pull this tim - ber 'fore the sun goes down____ Get it 'cross the riv - er 'fore the boss come round____ Drag it on down that dust - y road____ Come on Jerry,____ let's

My old Jerry is an Arkansas mule
Been everywhere and he ain't no fool
Weigh nine hundred and twenty-two
Done everything a poor mule can do.

Chorus: Haulin' timber, Lord, this timber's gotta roll . . .

Jerry's old shoulder was six foot tall
Pull more lumber than a freight can haul
Work gets heavy, old Jerry gets sore
Pull so much he won't pull no more.

Chorus: Haulin' timber, Lord, this timber's gotta roll . . .

Boss hit Jerry and he made him jump
Jerry ran, he kicked the boss on the rump
My old Jerry is a good old mule
If it hadda been me, Lord, I'd a-killed that fool.

Chorus: Haulin' timber, Lord, this timber's gotta roll . . .

The boss tried to shoot old Jerry in the head
Jerry ducked that bullet and he stomped him dead
Stomped that boss till I wanted to scream
Should have killed him 'cause he's so damn mean.

Chorus: Haulin' timber, Lord, this timber's gotta roll . . .

Probably the most widely recorded and sung ballad of America. It celebrates a folk hero, known for his strength and indomitableness. Typically American, the John Henry saga celebrates not the high-born, but a laborer, an outsized portrait of the men who built this country. Believed to be patterned on a steel-driver who drilled the Big Bend Tunnel of the Chesapeake and Ohio Railroad in West Virginia in 1872. Whether he was Negro or white, whether he lived or was fictional, John Henry has become a part of the American experience.

John Henry

Traditional

When John Hen-ry was a lit-tle ba-by, _____ He was set - tin' on his mam-my's knees, _____ Well, he stuck out his hand and he

grabbed a piece of steel Says, "It's gon-na be the death of me, Lord, Lord It's gon-na be the death of me."

John Henry said to his captain
"Well, a man ain't nothin' but a man
And before I let this steam-drill beat me down
I'll die with this hammer in my hand, Lord, Lord
Yes, I'll die with my hammer in my hand."

John Henry said to his shaker
"Well, now shaker why don't you sing?
'Cause I'm throwin' nine pounds from my hips on down
Just listen to the cold steel ring, Lord, Lord
Just listen to the cold steel ring."

John Henry said to his shaker
"Well, now shaker why don't you pray?
'Cause if my hammer miss that little piece of steel
Tomorrow be a buryin' day, Lord, Lord,
Tomorrow be a buryin' day."

Some said he was born in Texas
Some said he was born in Maine
But I don't give a damn where that poor boy was born
He was a steel-drivin' man, Lord, Lord
Now he was a steel-drivin' man.

The captain said to John Henry
"I believe the mountain's sinkin' in"
John Henry laughed at his captain and said
"It ain't nothin' but my hammer suckin' wind, Lord Lord
Ain't nothin' but my hammer suckin' wind."

Oh, the man that invented that steam drill
Thought he was mighty fine
John Henry made his fourteen feet
The steam drill only made nine, Lord, Lord
The steam drill only made nine.

Well, they took John Henry to the mountain
On the mountain top so high
He drove so hard he broke his poor heart
He laid down his hammer and died, Lord, Lord
He laid down his hammer and died.

Took John Henry to the graveyard
And they buried him in the sand
Yes and every locomotive come rollin' by
Said, "There lays a steel-drivin' man, Lord, Lord
There lays a steel-drivin' man."

153

An original by Josh White. He wrote the song with his Uncle Sonny in mind. "Jail break's due some day" is the only relieving note of hope in this prison plaint. Uncle Sonny died in prison and was buried near the rock pile that killed him. Josh's song is his epitaph.

Trouble

Music and Words by Josh White

white man, ___ And they locked me ___ in ___ the can. ___ Well, ___ they

took me ___ to ___ the stock-ade, ___ Would-n't give me no trial ___ And ___ the

judge, he said, "You black boy ___ for-ty years on the hard rock pile." Lord, I'm

trou-ble, ___ ___ trou-ble, ___ ___ Sure can't make ___ me stay ___ Lord, I'm ___

trou-ble,_____ trou-ble,_____ jail break due__ some day._____

Now I'm wearin' cold iron shackles
From my head down to my knees
And that mean old keeper
Lord, is all time kicking me.
Well, I went up to the walker
And the head-boss, too
And I said, "Please, all you big white folk
Won't you see what you can do."

Chorus: Lord, I'm trouble, trouble . . .

Well, the sheriff winked at the policeman
Says, "I won't forget you nohow
You better come back and see me again, boy
About forty years from now."
Well, I went back to the walker
He looked at me and said
"Buddy, don't you worry 'bout forty
'Cause in five years you'll be dead."

Final chorus:
Lord, I'm trouble, trouble
Makes me weep and moan
Lord, I'm trouble, trouble
Since the day I was born.
Lord I'm trouble, trouble
Sure won't make me stay
Lord, I'm trouble, trouble
Jail break due some day.

156

Ditties and Tunes

One of the most popular songs in the oral tradition in the South. The stubborn "little black bug" known to farmers everywhere in cotton country has been widely interpreted as a symbol of the Negro, indestructible and tenaciously holding onto life on the fruits of the soil.

Boll Weevil

Traditional

Have you heard the lat-est___ the lat-est of___ the song?___ It's 'bout them lit-tle Boll Wee-vils,___ picked up___ both___ feet___ and gone. Look-in' for a

home, _____ Just a-look-in' for a home. _____

Just look-in' for a home, _____ Just a-look-in' for a home _____

Just a-look-in' for a home _____ Just a-look-in' foi a home. _____

First time I saw the Boll Weevil he was sittin' on the square
Next time I saw the Boll Weevil he had his whole damn family there
He was a-lookin' for a home, just a-lookin' for a home.

The farmer took the Boll Weevil, put him in hot sand
The Weevil said to the farmer, I'll stand it like a man
'Cause it'll be my home, it'll be my home.

Farmer said to the Boll Weevil, what makes your head so red
The way I have been a-travelin' it's a wonder I ain't dead
Lookin' for a home, just a-lookin' for a home.

Chorus: Just a-lookin' for a home, just a-lookin' for a home . . .

The farmer took the Boll Weevil, put him in Paris green
Thank you, Mr. Farmer, the best I've ever seen
It'll be my home, it'll be my home.

Boll Weevil said to the farmer, man you'd better leave me alone
I et up all your cotton and now I'll eat your corn
I'll have a home, I'll have a home.

The farmer said to the merchant, I ain't got but one bale
And before I bring you that one, I'll fight and go to jail
And I'll have a home, I'll have a home.

The Boll Weevil said to the doctor, you'd better pour out all your pills
When I get through with this farmer he can't pay no doctor bills
'Cause he'll have no home, he'll have no home.

Chorus: Just a-lookin' for a home, just a-lookin' for a home . . .

The merchant got half the cotton, the Boll Weevil got the rest
Left the farmer's wife just one old cotton dress
And it was full of holes, it was full of holes.

Different chorus:
It was full of holes, it was full of holes
It was full of holes, it was full of holes.

If anybody asks you who in the hell wrote this song
A poor old workin' farmer with a pair of blue jeans on
Lookin' for a home, lookin' for a home.

Chorus: Just a-lookin' for a home, just a-lookin' for a home . . .

A widely known song that Josh has made his own, converting it into a sly little joke about waning sexual prowess. As "Sweet Thing" it was a Negro blues, but it spread quickly among Negro and white singers, into "Sugar Babe," "Crawdad" and dozens of variants. In World War I it was a rationing song: "What you gonna do when your shoes give out?"

What You Gonna Do?

New Music and Words by Josh White

What you gon-na do when your meat gives out, my ba-by____

What you gon-na do when the meat gives out__ my ho-ney____

What you gonna do when your shoes give out, my baby?
What you gonna do when your shoes give out, my honey?
My shoes get thin, I'm gonna quit the street
Take my chair and put a fan at my feet
For sometime.

What you gonna do when your chair gives out, my baby?
What you gonna do when your chair gives out, my honey?
When I've got no chair, no meat, no shoes
Gonna lay 'cross the bed with my head in the blues
For sometime.

Slats in the bed go blam-de-blam in the mornin'
Slats in the bed go blam-de-blam in the evenin'
Slats in the bed go blam-de-blam
But I'll go on sleepin' like I don't give a damn
For sometime.

What you gonna do when your man gives out, my baby?
What you gonna do when your man gives out, my honey?
First I'll grab my money, kick him off the place
Then I'll use the other man I had around just in case
For sometime.

161

A marching song for democracy. Done in the spirit of a Negro jubilee, the bright tempo and optimistic outlook make this song of World War II timeless in its impact.

Freedom Road

Music by Emerson Harper / Words by Langston Hughes

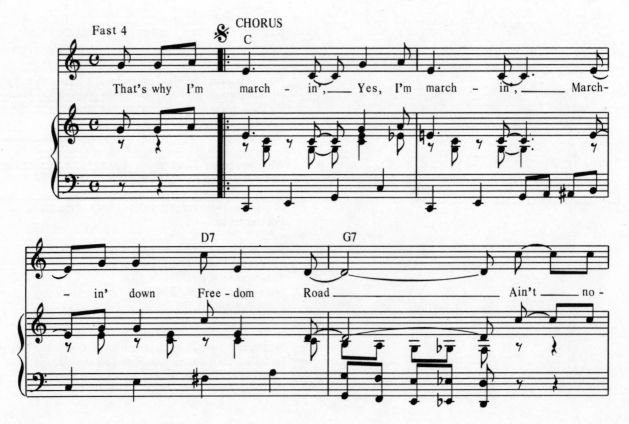

bo - dy gon - na stop me, There's no - bo - dy gon - na keep me from

march - in' down Free - dom Road. _____ Yes, I'm Road.

Hand me my gun, _____ Let _____ the bu - gle blow loud, _____

I'm on my way _____ with _____ my head up, proud, _____

One ___ ob - jec - tive _____ I've got in view, _____ is to

keep a - hold of free - dom, for ___ me and you. ___ That's why I'm

It ought to be plain as the nose on your face
There's room in this land for every race
Some folks think that freedom just ain't right
Those are the very people I want to fight.

Chorus: That's why I'm marchin', yes, I'm marchin' . . .

United we stand, divided we fall
Let's make this land safe for one and all
I've got a message and you know it's right
"Black and white together, unite and fight!"

Chorus: That's why I'm marchin', yes, I'm marchin' . . .

This song from slavery days has enjoyed great popularity among Southern Negroes and whites. Because of its dual meanings, "Raise a Ruckus" can be taken as either having fun or stirring up trouble. Thus this playful minstrel-show song has an undertone of protest and irony. Considered a "reel" in Josh White's home, it could not be sung there.

Raise a Ruckus

Traditional / New Music and Words by Josh White

Why don't you come a-long, lit-tle chil-dren, come a-long,

while the moon is shin-ing bright _____

Some folks say that a preacher won't steal
(Raise a ruckus tonight)
But I caught two in my cornfield
(Raise a ruckus tonight)
One had a shovel and one had a hoe
(Raise a ruckus tonight)
They were diggin' up potatoes by the row
(Raise a ruckus tonight).

Chorus: Why don't you come along, little children, come along . . .

'Way down yonder in Chitlin Switch
(Raise a ruckus tonight)
Bullfrog jumped from ditch to ditch
(Raise a ruckus tonight)
Bullfrog jumped from the bottom of the well
(Raise a ruckus tonight)
Swore, by God, he'd jump in hell
(Raise a ruckus tonight).

Chorus: Why don't you come along, little children, come along . . .

A tongue-in-cheek song about a woman who gave her favors too easily. A composed song of the Nineteen Forties, which the singer says "I love to perform."

Where Were You Baby

Note: This is a "talking blues."

I looked in ev - 'ry

bar - room, _____ and __ I searched from coast to coast, You were scarce as low cost hous-

ing baby When I need - ed you most, Where were you,

ba - by? When my heart went out,

you left me, ba - by. In all this dark - ness and doubt

1.2. (to Verses 2 & 3)

2) And I peeked thru fan -

3.

Verse 4

But to-

night, I think I'm gon-na take some good ad-vice,___ I'm gon-na look a-round and

find me some-bo-dy that's...Uh*(spoken)* real-ly nice___ And per-haps a ban-ker's

daugh-ter, if her pop-pa's a cuss.___ Well, I hope to do to her___

___ what her pop-pa does to us. And___ she'll have a fan-cy shack, a___

fan - cy Cad - il - lac, And stu - dy - in' to be ___ a

nym - pho - ma - ni - ac. ___ And ___ we'll have a lit - tle rye, ___ Play ___ a lit - tle gin,

Have a - noth - er rye, ___ and tune some mu - sic in. ___ Then we'll

have a - noth - er rye, ___ just to get a lit - tle glow ___ We'll

turn the lights down low, to keep the bulbs from get tin' hot! And we'll

play a lit-tle game called——— Yes, No, Why not? But —— to-

night I think I'm gon-na find me some-thing——— swell,——— so I can

wake up in the morn-ing——— Mis-'ra-ble as hell. When

but-ter costs a dol-lar, ___ and bread costs more than cake,

Come back soon, 'cause think of what a gal like you could make. ___ Come,

___ come, come, ba-by, ___ don't tell me ___ that we're through ___

'Cause this time, ___ ba-by, ___

I'd like to walk right out on you._____

2 I peeked through fancy boudoirs and I peeked through window grates
I only saw Republicans romancing Southern states
Where were you, baby, when my heart went out?
Well, you left me, baby, in all this darkness and doubt.

3 I tried to replace you with a streetwalker named Desire
Prices all up so high — hell, I couldn't afford to try her
It takes you, my baby, to put my fire out
Yes, you left me, baby, in all this darkness and doubt.

The tragicomic song of a man without enough money to buy the meal he wanted. This version was adapted and composed by Hy Zaret and Lou Singer in 1944, and thereafter Josh was the chief popularizer of the song. According to the folklorist Kenneth S. Goldstein, a Latin Professor at Harvard had written a ditty in 1850 called "The Lay of One Fishball." Twelve years later Francis James Child, the great authority on British ballads, composed a burlesque operetta in Italian on the song, called "Il Pesceballo." The "mock operetta" was translated into English by James Russell Lowell, the famous poet, and performed in Cambridge for the benefit of Union soldiers in the Civil War. The song and opera then dropped into obscurity, until 1944.

One Meat Ball

By Hy Zaret and Lou Singer

176

He told the waiter near at hand
The simple dinner he had planned
The guests were startled one and all
To hear the waiter loudly call.

Chorus:
One meatball, one meatball
Hey, this here gent wants one meatball.

You know the little man felt ill at ease
He said, "Some bread, sir, if you please"
The waiter hollered down the hall
"You gets no bread with one meatball."

Chorus:
One meatball, one meatball
Well, you gets no bread with one meatball.

The little man felt very bad
One meatball was all he had
And in his dream he hears that call
"You gets no bread with one meatball."

Chorus:
One meatball (and no spaghetti), one meatball
　　(and no spaghetti)
Well, you gets no bread with one meatball.

A musical setting from a poem by Paul Laurence Dunbar. The singer
learned it from Josephine Premise.

Woman Sure Is a Curious Critter

Very freely

Wom - an
sure is a cur' - ious crit - ter, and there ain't no doubt in that. She's a

mess of fun-ny ca-pers, from her slip-pers to her hat.____ If you try to un-der-stand____ her you fail, just up and say, Ain't a bit of use to try to un-der-stand a wo-man's ways.

I'm not complaining, but I'm just a-settin' down
My own observations as I cast my eye around
If you ask me to prove it, I can do it without a doubt
'Cause there ain't no better example than this very wife of mine.

In the very heat of midnight, when I'm sleepin' good and sound
I can hear a sorta rustlin' and somebody movin' round
So I sez, "Liz, what you doin'?" and she frowns and shakes her head
"Shut your mouth, I'm only turnin' the children in the bed."

So she shakes 'em and she twists 'em
And she turns 'em round about
I don't see how those children ever keep from hollerin', "Ouch, look out"
That's my gal.

When it's just about time for wakenin' on the dawn of Judgment Day
Seems like I could hear old Gabriel lay his trumpet down and say
"Who's that walkin' 'round so easy down on earth amongst the dead?"
It'll be Liz up a-turnin' the children in the bed.

One of the most interesting folk tales in American Negro music. A song popular in Southern jails and on chain-gangs during their most brutal period before World War I. The Lomaxes and John Greenway have found the song a symbolic statement of the indomitableness of the human spirit, the courage of the Negro in the face of white justice. "Gray Goose" has been compared to the fourteenth-century "Cutty Wren," the peasants' symbol of fighting oppression. Josh heard the song from a Blind Willie, whom he heard playing a Jew's harp on a bridge at Key West, Florida. Josh sees the parable as one of God turning his back on the preacher-hunter for trying to kill any living thing on a Sunday.

Gray Goose

And he carried along a shotgun (Lord, Lord, Lord)
And along came a gray goose (Lord, Lord, Lord)
Well, he ups to his shoulder . . .
And he pulls back the trigger . . .
And the gun went off boo-loo . . .
And down came the gray goose . . .
He was six weeks a-fallin' . . .
Then we had a feather-pickin' . . .
Well, your wife and my wife . . .
Your wife and my wife . . .
They put him on to parboil . . .
He was six weeks a-boilin' . . .
Then they put him on the table . . .

And the forks couldn't stick him . . .
Oh, well, the knife couldn't cut him . . .
Then they took him to the saw mill . . .
And he broke the saw's teeth out . . .
He broke the saw's teeth out . . .
Then they took him to the hog pen . . .
Man, the hogs couldn't eat him . . .
And the last time I seen him . . .
He was flyin' across the ocean . . .
With a long string of goslings . . .
They were all going "Quack, quack" . . .
That's the story of the gray goose . . .
I says, "The hell with the gray goose" . . .

180

Children's Songs

Is there anyone in the United States who has not heard this traditional
playparty tune?

Skip to My Lou

Traditional

Flies in the buttermilk, shoo-fly-shoo *(3 times)*
Skip to my lou my darling.

Chorus: Lou, lou, skip to my lou . . .

Old gray mare has lost its shoe *(3 times)*
Skip to my lou my darling.

Chorus: Lou, lou, skip to my lou . . .

Lost my partner, what'll I do? *(3 times)*
Skip to my lou my darling.

Chorus: Lou, lou, skip to my lou . . .

I'll find another one prettier than you *(3 times)*
Skip to my lou my darling.

Chorus: Lou, lou, skip to my lou . . .

A children's playparty song with a jaunty tempo that the young ones love.
Leadbelly made one version famous as "Green Corn."

Black-Eyed Susan

(OR GREEN CORN)

Traditional

Wake snake, day's a-break-in' Peas in the pot and the hoe cakes a-bak-in', Green corn___ Green corn.___

Chorus:
Green corn, come along Charlie
Green corn, come along Charlie
Green corn, green corn.
Stand around, stand around the jimmyjohn
Stand around, stand around the jimmyjohn
Green corn, green corn.

Black-eyed Susie went a-huckleberry pickin'
Boys got drunk and Susie took a-lickin'.

Chorus: Green corn, come along Charlie . . .

Some got drunk and some got boozy
I went home with Black-Eyed Susie.

Chorus: Green corn, come along Charlie . . .

Up red oak and down salt water
Some old man's gonna lose his daughter.

Chorus: Green corn, green corn.

All I want in this creation
Is a good-lookin' gal with a big plantation.

Chorus: Green corn, come along Charlie . . .

183

Age does not wither nor custom stale the best in folk music. Like timeless heirlooms, the best songs live forever, retaining their universal appeal.
First recorded in a British broadside in the middle of the sixteenth century, this is still popular with children throughout the English-speaking world.

Froggie Went A-Courtin'

(OR MR. FROG)

Traditional

Frog went a-court-in' and he did ride, Ah - hah, Ah -

hah. Mis-ter Frog went a-court-in' and he did ride, A

sword and a pis-tol by his side. Ah-hah, mm hmm.

Rode up to Miss Mouse's door, ah-ha! ah-ha!
Rode up to Miss Mouse's door
He knocked and knocked till his fist got sore
Ah-ha! Ah-ha!

(*Follow same style*)
Set Miss Mouse on his knee . . .
Said, "Miss Mousie, will you marry me?" . . .

"Without my Uncle Rat's consent . . .
I wouldn't marry the President." . . .

Uncle Rat gave his consent . . .
The weasel wrote the publishment . . .

Where shall the weddin' supper be . . .
Out in the woods in a holler tree . . .

First came in was a lady bug . . .
She had some whisky in her jug . . .

Next came in was Mister Tick . . .
He ate so much that it made him sick . . .

Next came in was a bumblebee . . .
He tried to dance with a two-legged flea . . .

Mister Frog he went down to the lake . . .
And there he got swallowed by a big black snake . . .

This is the end of one, two, three . . .
The snake, the frog and Miss Mousie . . .

The household riddle song, a ditty beloved by children all around the country. Josh has found it as popular with his own children and grandchildren as he has with audiences from coast to coast.

What Are Little Boys Made Of

Traditional

What are lit-tle boys made of?

What are little girls made of?
What are little girls made of?
Sugar and spice and everything nice
That's what little girls are made of.

What are young women made of?
What are young women made of?
Rings and jings and they're all fine things
That's what young women are made of.

What are young men made of?
What are young men made of?
Thorns and briars and they're all damn liars
That's what young men are made of.

What are old men made of?
What are old men made of?
Whisky, brandy, anything you've got handy
That's what old men are made of.

What are old women made of?
What are old women made of?
Moans and groans in their old aching bones
That's what old women are made of.

Index of First Lines

Discography

JOSH WHITE's first known recording session took place in New York City on April 6, 1932, and he has since made several hundred records. On early releases he was known as "Joshua White, The Singing Christian" or as "Pinewood Tom." His work has appeared on all of the following labels (American except as noted): ABC-Paramount, Asch, Banner, Blue Note, Brunswick (English), Columbia, Conqueror, Decca, Elektra, Harmony, Jazz Parade (English), Keynote, London, Mayor (Italian), Melodisc (English), Melotone, Mercury, Metronome (Swedish), Musicraft, Oriole, Perfect, Romeo, Stinson, Vocalion and Vogue (French). Josh has also recorded for the Library of Congress and Columbia University in New York City. A complete listing of all these recordings would fill several pages and many of them are impossible to obtain now or are collector's items. Such a listing may be secured from *The Discophile*, published in England at 116 London Road, Barking, Essex. The records listed below are current, well known and obtainable.

JOSH WHITE SINGS THE BLUES
(Stinson SLP-14)

Baby, Baby
Miss Otis Regrets
Dupree
Fare Thee Well
Number 12 Train
Mean Mistreatin' Woman
When I Lay Down and Die Do Die
I Got a Head Like a Rock
Cotton-Eyed Joe
Jim Crow Train
Strange Fruit

JOSH WHITE SINGS
(Stinson SLP-15)

One Meat Ball
Motherless Children
St. James Infirmary
Careless Love
Outskirts of Town
Well, Well, Well
T.B. Blues
Joshua Fit the Battle of Jericho
Hard Times
Evil-Hearted Man

JOSH WHITE AT TOWN HALL
(Mercury MG-20672)

Outskirts of Town
I Know Where I Am Goin'
Foggy Dew
Rising Sun
Hard Time Blues
The Lass with the Delicate Air
Half as Much
Pastures of Plenty
What Ya Gonna Do
Green Grass Grows All Around

THE BEGINNING
(Mercury MG-20724)

In the Evening
Key to the Kingdom
Howling Wolf
Job: 19
Hoe Boys, Can't You Line 'Em
Evil-Hearted Man
My Father Is a Husband Man
Blues Come from Texas
Sit Down Servant
'Lijah

SINGLE
(Mercury 71934)

Bonbons, Chocolates and
    Chewing Gum
He's Got the Whole World in His
    Hands

JOSH WHITE
(Decca DL-8665)

I Gave My Love a Cherry
Molly Malone
Green Grass Growing All Around
The Lass with the Delicate Air
Lord Randall, My Son
Watercress
Waltzing Matilda
John Henry
Strange Fruit
Nobody Knows You
        When You're Down and Out
Evil-Hearted Man
Jelly, Jelly
Sometime
Frankie and Johnny
Back Water Blues
Josh and Bill Blues

A JOSH WHITE PROGRAM
(London LL-1341)

Call Me Darling
Like a Natural Man
The Lass with the Delicate Air
Barbara Allen
Foggy, Foggy Dew
I'm Gonna Move to the
    Outskirts of Town
Apples, Peaches and Cherries
Take a Girl Like You
Waltzing Matilda
The Lonesome Road
Molly Malone
He Never Said a Mumblin' Word

THE JOSH WHITE STORIES: VOLUME 1
(ABC-Paramount ABC-124)

Boll Weevil
Watercress
What You Gonna Do?
I'm a Mean Mistreater
Frankie and Johnny
The House of the Rising Sun
Dupree
Cottoneye Joe
Nobody Knows You
    When You're Down and Out
When I Lay Down
Hard Times Blues
He Never Said a Mumblin' Word

THE JOSH WHITE STORIES: VOLUME 2
(ABC-Paramount ABC-166)

Good Morning, Blues
The Gray Goose
You Won't Let Me Go
Don't Smoke in Bed
Trouble in Mind
Sometimes I Feel
    Like a Motherless Child
Two Little Fishes
    (and Five Loaves of Bread)
I Know Moonlight
Red River
I Had a Woman
Fine and Mellow
Strange Fruit

JOSH WHITE—LIVE
(ABC-Paramount, Mono ABC-407,
Stereo ABCS-407)

Betty and Dupree
Wandering

Got a Head Like a Rock
Apples, Peaches and Cherries
You Know Baby
Freedom Road
Scarlet Ribbons
The Man Who Couldn't Walk Around
Where Were You Baby
    When My Heart Went Out
Sam Hall
Strange Fruit

JOSH AT MIDNIGHT
(Elektra EKL-102)

St. James Infirmary
Raise a Ruckus
Scandalize My Name
Jesus Gonna Make Up My Dyin' Bed
Timber
Jelly, Jelly
One Meat Ball
Joshua Fit the Battle of Jericho
Don't Lie Buddy
Number 12 Train
Peter
Takin' Names

JOSH
(Elektra EKL-114)

Midnight Special
Miss Otis Regrets
Halleleu
Woman Sure Is a Curious Critter
Prison-Bound Blues
Gloomy Sunday
Ball and Chain Blues
One for My Baby
Jim Crow Train
Told My Captain
So Soon in the Mornin'
Bury My Body

JOSH WHITE 25TH ANNIVERSARY ALBUM
(Elektra EKL-123)

The Story of John Henry
Black Girl
Free and Equal Blues
Live the Life
Sam Hall
Where Were You, Baby?
Delia's Gone
Run, Mona, Run
You Don't Know My Mind

CHAIN GANG SONGS
(Elektra, Mono EKL-158,
Stereo EKS-7158)

Trouble
'Twas on a Monday
Going Home, Boys
Nine Foot Shovel
Crying Who? Crying You
Dip Your Fingers in the Water
The Old Ship of Zion
Mary Had a Baby
Did You Ever Love a Woman
Every Time I Feel the Spirit

SPIRITUALS & BLUES
(Elektra, Mono EKL-193,
Stereo EKS-7193)

Southern Exposure
Red Sun
Silicosis Blues
Black Snake
Things About Coming My Way
I've Got That Pure Religion
Nobody Knows the Trouble I've Seen
I Know King Jesus
Just a Closer Walk with Thee
I Don't Intend to Die in Egypt Land

THE HOUSE I LIVE IN
(Elektra, Mono EKL-203,
Stereo EKS-7203)

Good Morning Blues
Johnny Has Gone for a Soldier
Waltzing Matilda
When I Lay Down and Die
Mean Mistreater
Blind Man Stood on the Road and Cried
Freedom Road
Man Who Couldn't Walk Around
T.B. Blues
The House I Live In

EMPTY BED BLUES
(Elektra, Mono EKL-211,
Stereo EKS-7211)

Empty Bed Blues
Mother on That Train
Bottle Up and Go
Backwater Blues
Baby Baby Blues
Lord Have Mercy
Home In That Rock
Paul and Silas
His Eye Is on the Sparrow
That Suits Me